CHILDREN'S NURSE

G000135630

Nurse Linda Grey travels to Portugal to look
after four-year-old Jacinto but her modern ideas
meet with strong opposition from the boy's
father, the handsome Marquez de Filano.

CHILDREN'S NURSE

BY

KATHRYN BLAIR

MILLS & BOON LIMITED
London . Sydney . Toronto

First published in Great Britain 1957
by Mills & Boon Limited, 15–16 Brook's Mews,
London W1A 1DR under the title 'Valley of Flowers'

ISBN 0 263 73465 X

Set in Monophoto Times 9 on 9½ pt.

Made and printed in Great Britain by
Richard Clay (The Chaucer Press) Ltd,
Bungay, Suffolk

CHAPTER ONE

FROM Portão the road wound among the low mountains for about fifteen miles and then, in a series of graceful curves among vineyards and rolling pasture lands, it descended towards Merida, the only town in the Valle das Flores. Linda sat in the back of the chauffeur-driven, richly-upholstered limousine and looked out with some wonder and a degree of apprehension at the quintas—those big country houses set among billows of flowers and orchards—at the pergolas draped with vines, at wheat which was yellowing in the spring sunshine, at forests of cork trees on the hillsides, and at a gently winding river with a cottage here and there on its banks.

So this was the Valley of Flowers! It was all Mrs Bayes had promised, and Linda decided that the rest of what the woman had told her was no doubt equally true. During the two-hour drive from Lisbon to Portão she had found herself liking the youthfully middle-aged Mrs Bayes who knew the Marquez de Filano so well that he had asked her to meet his son's new nurse. Eve Bayes had, in fact, made Linda's arrival in Lisbon very pleasant.

At the airport they had coffee and sandwiches, and by the time they had come out to the big black car with a coat-of-arms on its door, Linda had learned quite a lot about her prospective employer and the Palacio Filano. Eve Bayes was the wife of a fairly rich man who had both business and social contacts with the Marquez, and as the car took the road to Portão, where she lived, Mrs Bayes had expatiated upon the pleasures of living in the mellow Valle das Flores.

'My husband and I have a small villa in Merida, and we often go there for the weekend. When my daughter comes over from England for her school holidays I spend the whole time there with her, and her father comes as often as he can. The Marquez is a bit stiff, but he's very kind, particularly to young people.' Her bright glance took in Linda's trim figure in the blue suit and white cotton blouse, and her beautiful wavy cornsilk hair. 'I'm not quite sure whether you're young enough to qualify, though. How old are you?'

'Twenty-two.'

'The Marquez wanted someone about thirty, but you were

the only applicant who had a smattering of Portuguese, and as you were highly recommended by Rawson Hall he decided to take you on. By the way,' she smiled conspiratorially, 'I was the one who recommended that he get in touch with Rawson Hall, so don't let me down in any way, will you? You're not likely to have any trouble with little Jacinto. He's really quite a model child.'

'Who's been looking after him?'

'An Englishwoman, but she was old and had to retire. These ancient families are keen on the English nurse-governess trained on modern lines, but they also have their own ideas about the child's upbringing. It's best to give in to them most of the time. Did you take the full two years at Rawson?'

Linda nodded. 'Yes, and I've had nearly another two years at a child guidance clinic. Then I wanted a chance of living abroad, so I wrote to the principal, and within a month she had this job to offer. I couldn't believe it!'

The older woman looked at her appraisingly. 'You're really keen, aren't you? I'm English, too, so I know how you're feeling at this moment. A little wound up, but very happy. Mind if I hand out a spot of advice?'

'Of course not, Mrs Bayes.'

'Well, take it slowly, and be very careful not to tread on any toes. The Marquez is very much the nobleman and no one ever contradicts him, not even his aunt, who runs the household. The little boy is nearly four and he never plays with other children; to you, naturally, that will seem appalling, but do for heaven's sake soak in the atmosphere of the place before you suggest anything revolutionary. After all,' with humour, 'you can't hope to anglicise the Portuguese. How did you get to know the language, by the way?'

'My father put in a year at Oporto for his firm. I was only ten at the time, and I had to do my schooling with some other English children in a private house. I don't know why, but I clung to the Portuguese I'd picked up. It wasn't much, but it should get me by.' She waved a hand to indicate the warm countryside through which they were passing. 'I don't remember anything like this. We children had to keep to our own garden.'

'It's a marvellous country,' commented Mrs. Bayes, 'and the people are both simple and remarkable. I think you'll like living here.'

6

'I'm sure of it!' But Linda's blue glance was a little anxious. 'How do I address the Marquez?'

'Just call him senhor—that's all he'll expect as you're English. You'll hear others call him Excellency, but it's merely a form of politeness. I've even been called Excellency myself! As for everything else—well, you're intelligent. Just feel your way. And if you're in doubt at all, get in touch with me. I shall be seeing you soon, anyway. John and I have been invited to lunch at the Palacio next Sunday, and I'll make a point of coming to your quarters. By then, you'll have found out a few things!'

Yes, Linda had felt decidedly better for the meeting with Mrs Bayes, and she was grateful to her unknown employer for his consideration in asking the Englishwoman to welcome her. The car had run through the streets of Portão and stopped at a white house with curly red tiles and grilles at the windows. Mrs Bayes had wished her well and said goodbye, and the car had moved on towards the mountains and Merida.

Now Linda Grey looked out at stone walls covered with roses, and she glimpsed shuttered windows and courtyards covered with flowering vines. It was four o'clock and the streets were deserted except for a vendor here and there who slept beside a pile of yellow and white poppies, or a tray of vegetables near the kerbside.

It was unbelievable that she had left England only this morning. There, she had walked in a cold wind and under grey skies to the plane; and here she was in the brilliant and beautiful Valle das Flores where the midday heat sent people to their beds! The transition was almost too swift and abrupt, but it was for just such a change that she had been yearning.

She had left home two years ago, when her father had married again. It wasn't that she didn't like Charlotte—considering the difference in their ages and temperaments they got along extraordinarily well—but it was only natural that an adult step-daughter would be in the way. Charlotte had brought a new set of friends to the house, and by a natural process Linda had become a visitor instead of a member of the household. She had found herself feeling a little adrift. In the course of time she had received letters from old friends who had been at Rawson Hall with her, letters with exotic postmarks, and she had known that stirring which so often comes to a girl who wonders if she is being left behind. Why not travel, or at least live somewhere else for a while?

Her brother, comfortably married and established in the north of England, had considered it a bit much that Linda should think it might be more exciting to live in Portugal than in England, but Mr Grey was all for the change. At odd times during the last twenty years he had had to put in several spells abroad, and he remembered almost with nostalgia his year in the lovely old city of Oporto. Though he would have preferred Linda to marry some presentable young man and settle down in England, he was in favour of her giving the post as nurse to the motherless son of the Marquez de Filano a trial. By plane, she would be only a few hours away; nothing to it, he said.

And so far, there had been nothing to it, or almost nothing. The big car ran smoothly and opulently, the uniformed chauffeur, who was short and thick-set and very conscious of his position, looked straight ahead and spoke not at all. And the countryside, with its cloistered houses and profusions of blossoms under an azure sky, floated past like a mirage. This could go on for ever, she felt. But it didn't.

They by-passed the main part of the town and followed a granite road which climbed very gradually among vineyards and orchards. There came a long stretch bordered by mulberry trees, and then, to the right, the mulberries gave way to giant veronicas and prunus bushes, oleanders and Kentia palms. Then, almost imperceptibly, there came a wall covered with rust-red bougainvillea and yellow lemon-vine, a tremendously high wall above which olives and pines, quince and jacaranda tangled themselves together with abandon. By now, Linda was prepared for the wait while the wrought-iron gates were opened, and for the sweep through massive portals on to a gravel drive between pencil cedars and wide green lawns. But she never did quite recover from the first visual impact of the Palacio Filano.

Seeing it there, set back against billows of green trees, it was impossible to take in the whole of it at one go. The pale mellowed stone, the dozens of small Gothic windows, the many clear-cut steeples outlined in filigree, the great entrance with its façade of delicate sculpture and the family crest above the door, the series of stone archways along the front which created a fine cool terrace, the courtyard with its fountain and ornate stone flower-holders dripping with star-flowers and aubretias and portulaca ... they were impossible of absorption.

For a frightening moment her heart was in her throat and she almost said aloud: 'Good heavens, I can't live here. I can't!'

But common sense took hold. In such a castle she would be but one small soul, negligible in herself. It would be fun to learn how these people lived and to have charge of such an important little boy, and after all, there was a considerable salary attached to the job. She had come here for two things—the salary and the chance of living abroad; in return for them she would give of her best, and the way to do so was to remain fairly detached from the expensive surroundings. As she was an alien here, that should be easy.

The car rounded the fountain and drew up at the foot of a semi-circular sweep of shallow steps. The big door opened and a manservant came down to open the car door. He bowed politely and spoke in Portuguese.

'Please enter, senhora. The driver will attend to the luggage.'

Linda went ahead, up the half a dozen steps, across the star-shaped mosaic set in marble, and into a large hall where it was dim and cloistral. Fluted pillars supported a baroque ceiling, and a wide staircase with a heavily-carved handrail mounted to a long landing which was panelled on the hall side with fretted oak. Beyond this low panelled wall Linda could see portraits on the further wall, and two arched windows curtained with gold damask.

Again in Portuguese, the servant said, 'Please come this way, senhora. I will take you to your room. The Senhora de Filano will see you soon.'

Haltingly, she asked, 'And the little boy? Where is he?'

A shrug. 'The Senhora de Filano will tell you. Please?'

So she went with him, up the stairs and along the corridor, turned to the right and along another corridor and eventually followed him into a large, sumptuous, but somewhat soulless apartment which was furnished with golden wood, lilac silk curtains and bedspread and a rich Persian carpet. She stood in the centre of the room while the two suitcases were brought in and placed conveniently for unpacking, but when the door had closed behind the two servants she let out a breath which seemed to have been imprisoned too long.

She was here at the Palacio Filano, and apparently her coming was unmomentous, but she was not dismayed. On the whole, the experience of arriving had been less unnerving than she had anticipated, and there was certainly no question of their having forgotten her existence. Take everything in your stride, Linda, my pet!

Unconsciously tiptoeing, she drew open the french door and went out to the balcony. Below, she saw borders of geraniums and heliotrope, a pond covered with lilies, statuary in a wide arbour, and . . . surely not!

A man in white was strolling in the distance across one of the outer reaches of the lawn. He carried a golf club like a rifle over one shoulder and presently he stopped to address a ball. A neat shot, but slightly angled; the ball found home in a riot of jasmine. Linda smiled, felt decidedly easier round the heart. The man was a golfer, and not a good one. That made him human.

She heard a sound in the room and turned about to face a maidservant of uncertain age. The woman was thin, her skin a little leathery, and her dark hair was drawn into a severe topknot; she wore a long black cotton frock, a white pleated apron and felt slippers.

Slowly, in English, she said 'Doña Velira will see you now, Miss Grey. Please to come downstairs to the sala.'

'Wouldn't it be best to put on my uniform first?'

The woman looked blank. 'The dress for the nurse? Perhaps not today.'

'Very well. I'm ready.'

Linda took a fleeting glance at herself in the cheval mirror, ran a hand over her hair and followed the woman out into the corridor and down the long lanes overlooked by portraits to the head of the stairs. At the foot of the staircase they turned right, and after tapping at a tall door the servant turned a crystal handle and stood aside for Linda to enter.

The room was of more moderate dimensions than Linda had expected, and in spite of handsome white and gilt furniture upholstered in red and cream striped silk, had an almost homely air. The normal English sitting-room would have been lost in a corner of it, but no doubt it was one of the smaller rooms in the Palacio. Not that Linda gave it much attention. Her glance had naturally been drawn at once to Senhora de Filano.

Again English was spoken. 'You may go, Lupe, and remember that I do no wish to be disturbed.' And when the door had closed, 'How do you do, Miss Grey. Please sit down.'

The voice was foreign and imperious, typical of the woman who sat behind a small table that winked and glittered with silver and fragile china. The Senhora de Filano had fine oval features which had once been beautiful, and dark, opaque-looking eyes which were surprisingly large when she flipped back those heavy lids. Her skin was pale and lined, and the ageing neck was partly disguised by a collaret of pearls which fastened with a large emerald in the front. Her dress was the inevitable black, and though expensive and fairly new it had a Victorian look. Or perhaps it was the black hair thickly spread with grey which was piled high in soft rolls on the top of her head and fastened with an ornamental jet comb that created the atmosphere. Certainly Linda felt she had stepped back from the twentieth century, and the sensation was uncanny.

She sat stiffly in the chair indicated, opposite the senhora, waited politely for developments. But the older woman was in no hurry. Obviously, she had handled such situations many times and had perfected her approach. She poured coffee but did not hand over Linda's cup. She sat back, clasped her bony, beringed hands in front of her and briefly unshuttered the dark eyes.

'I see you do not wear a uniform, Miss Grey,' she said politely.

'If you wish, I can put it on for you at once,' Linda replied quickly. 'It's a uniform I'm proud to wear.'

'But you will not wear it,' said the senhora, with gentle emphasis. 'You will never wear it, you understand? The Marquez grew very tired of seeing our old nurse in her drab brown, and I have decided that dark, discreet frocks are better. There is nothing to equal the black day dress for any woman, whatever her age and calling.'

'At Rawson Hall,' Linda returned, with a hesitant smile, 'one of the first things we learnt was the value of neat uniform. Our summer one was slate-blue linen with white collar and cuffs, and I'm sure you'd approve of it, senhora.'

'No uniform,' stated Senhora de Filano. 'This is a point on which I insist!'

Just in time, Linda remembered Mrs Bayes' advice. She smiled again and said nothing. The senhora used the pause by handing to Linda her cup of coffee and pushing forward the sugar bowl. When she sat back the thin, slightly hooked nose seemed to quiver as if at the distant scent of battle.

'I must tell you what it is necessary for you to know about this household. I am related to the Marquez only by marriage to his father's brother. Until his wife died, only two months after Jacinto was born, I kept up my own establishment in Merida, even though I was a widow. However, my own children were grown up and I was needed here; I have made my home with the Marquez and guided the training of the small Jacinto.' She paused. 'The Palacio is very strange to you, Miss Grey?'

'Yes, of course. It's immense and beautiful.'

'Most of it is very old, and the estate covers much of the Valle das Flores. The de Filanos have been here for hundreds of years, and for the Portuguese it is a great honour to serve them. You understand?'

Linda nodded. 'I feel very lucky to have been chosen. I'll do my best.'

'It is a great pity you are so young, but perhaps that will make you more . . . what is the word, pliable? You will understand the more readily how I wish you to care for Jacinto. The old nurse, we found, had become set . . . what my nephew calls rabugenta. Creaky, no?'

Linda smiled. 'Cranky. Possibly that's how one gets after bringing up many children successfully.'

The senhora had not smiled. 'But that will not do for the Palacio. We know what we wish for Jacinto, and when we give orders the nurse must obey.'

'Very well, senhora.'

'Good. Now for your duties. Because we thought it necessary first to become acquainted with you, Jacinto is today at the house of my daughter; he will return tomorrow morning. He occupies the bedroom next to your own and there is a communicating door, which must be kept open all night. For the first day or two I will watch that you supervise him correctly—the meals, the sleeping, the bath, the prayers, the walks, the small lessons. There are certain things we consider important which may not be important elsewhere. You will learn them.'

'Yes, senhora.'

'For instance, he has many clothes so it is not necessary for

12

him to wear anything that becomes in the least soiled. Also, you must note his temperature each night.'

'Oh, but surely . . .'

The senhora lifted one of those useless-looking but nevertheless indomitable hands, and she smiled pointedly. 'The temperature in children is an indication of their fitness. You will do this.'

'Very well, senhora.'

'You have questions?'

Linda had necessarily become so much on her guard that she almost said no. But her spirit was not quite daunted. 'I notice the lawns are very beautiful and there seems to be no provision for a little boy's needs. Does Jacinto have a playroom, senhora?'

'There is a day nursery opposite your bedrooms; it will be in your care. In the open air Jacinto goes only for walks.'

'Is that his father's idea?' Linda asked unwisely.

The elegant old face tightened a little. 'I have two sons and a daughter, Miss Grey. My daughter is the admirable wife of a lawyer in Merida and my elder son is a doctor. The younger son . . .' Her smile was affectionate but for the first time uncertain, 'knows much about mining emeralds in Brazil. I am confident of my ability to direct the life of my nephew's son.'

'I'm sorry. I shall have to adjust my notions a little.'

The senhora nodded, aloofly. 'There is one thing you must never forget. Jacinto is a de Filano; he cannot be as other children.'

Linda looked at the woman and realised the utter futility of even seeming to argue with her. The Senhora de Filano, herself of a proud and arrogant family, was saturated with code and customs, the rigid etiquette which could only survive in a place such as this. The poor little chap didn't stand an earthly.

She drank her coffee, wondered if it would ever be possible to get a cup of tea in this extravagant castle which appeared to house a man and his small son, an aunt and a regiment of servants.

'I think that is all,' said the senhora dismissively. 'You will take your meals in the nursery with Jacinto and if you wish for late supper you may have it in your room. Oh, and I must tell you this. Always, with the senhorito, you will use the main doors of the Palacio—never the servants' doors. Alone, you may please yourself. You may go, Miss Grey, but have the

13

kindness to be ready for an interview with the Marquez. He will send for you.'

Linda escaped into the hall, closed the door and stood there breathing rather heavily and feeling slightly woolly in the head. So that was Doña Velira, the aunt of the Marquez, and the great-aunt of a little boy who wasn't yet four. The woman's English was good, but Linda would have wagered that the Senhora de Filano had never left Portugal. She simply didn't know that there was a world in which the de Filanos were not even thought of; she had grown up in this vicinity, leading the confined velvety life of the landowning rich. Her husband had probably been chosen for her and she had been serenely dependent, as such women were. And she had grown old within the same limits, wanting nothing more either for herself or for her children. But with age such women were likely to become fanatically narrow in outlook. Obviously she could be pleasant so long as she was getting her own way, but what if one crossed her, even mildly?

Slowly, Linda went upstairs and back to her bedroom. The training at Rawson Hall had been modern and had certainly not taken into account the occasional distinguished foreign family who might engage one of their graduates. There were English families who fell over one another to snap up the trained nurses, and Linda was beginning to think she might have been better off with one of them. Certainly an Englishwoman would have been overjoyed at the chance of relinquishing her problem children to someone who had been trained to cope.

Still, this was an experience, and the place definitely had something that others didn't. The whole Valley of Flowers was warm and relaxing, and as well as its age and architectural beauty, the Palacio had some thrilling element in its composition. One could lean from the balcony in this west wing and look along at the other balconies, at the shaped windows, the finely-wrought steeples at the other end of the edifice, and feel that indefinable something which must be the spirit of the place. A strong, compelling spirit. Yes, decided Linda with only slight reservations, so far she was glad she had come.

She unpacked and hung away her clothes, found a massive bathroom in veined green marble with a black floor, and washed with the sandalwood soap provided. She dried on a lush towel, took a peep into a linen cupboard where, in an oven-like atmosphere, numbers of small pants and vests were airing.

Back in her own room she used cosmetics and brushed her hair, and then as it was growing dark she switched on the lights and took a renewed interest in the room. How long ago had it been furnished, she wondered. Fifty or sixty years, perhaps, with new curtains about ten years ago. The lilac damask was heavy and rich, but an oldish person's taste. This room had certainly not been redecorated by little Jacinto's mother. And what about the boy's room?

Linda tried the communicating door and found it unlocked. She went inside the room and switched on the lights. She saw the bed, in dark wood against a ruched blue velvet drape on the wall, blue velvet curtains, a low tapestry chair, a big carved wardrobe and dressing chest, a built-in cupboard which presumably held toys, a book-case and a small desk which looked very new. A desk, and he was not yet four!

The furry pink edge-to-edge carpet was the only evidence that the room might be a child's. To Linda, it looked a rather pathetic attempt by someone who was completely overwhelmed by the Palacio's grandeur. Had the previous nurse insisted on it?

She was scarcely back in her room when a manservant knocked and asked her to come down to the library; he would show her the way. Linda braced herself, recalled the inexpert stroke with a golf club and hoped it was characteristic. Once more she reached the hall and was shown into a room, a different room this time.

There were two windows and walls of books, dark red carpeting, a really breathtaking desk with grapes and leaves trailing across the rich dark sides, and a couple of deep easy chairs as well as the leather desk chair. And there was a man in light trousers and a black cashmere sweater.

He turned round from the window, gazed at Linda for a long moment and showed dazzling white teeth in a smile. And he was so utterly handsome, so completely unexpected with his curly dark brown hair and smooth brown skin, the careless ease with which he stood, and the contrasting brightness of his glance, that Linda smiled back without the least hesitation. Phew, what a relief!

'You are the new nurse for Jacinto?' he asked.

'Yes, senhor.'

'But you are so pretty. What are they thinking of in

15

England, to send away such girls? But it is our gain, yes?'

'I hope so,' she answered demurely.

He clicked his heels and bowed. 'I am Enrico de Filano. Please sit down. Would you like some wine?'

'No, thank you.'

He came forward, and if anything his looks were even more shattering as he came into the glow from the big lamp on the desk. 'You have arrived this afternoon, Miss . . . er . . .?'

'Grey,' she supplied. 'I arrived soon after four.'

'I would have been here to greet you,' he said, 'but I did not know about your arrival. I was out.'

'Practising golf,' she murmured. 'I saw you.'

Again the devastating smile. 'So that is why I shoot the ball anywhere but into the hole! You are watching and I feel it because I am sensitive to such things. Perhaps we Portuguese are not so good at golf, but we excel at some things. Do not forget that!'

'I won't.'

He stood there, leaning against the desk and resting his rather disturbing glance on the pale gold hair. He said, 'You are so different from the old nurse—not that I knew her well. You have spoken with Doña Velira?'

'Yes, soon after I arrived.'

'And she approves of you?'

'I wouldn't say that.'

'But you must make her approve of you,' he said with urgency. He leaned nearer and lowered his voice conspiratorially. 'I will give you a hint. Say always, "Yes, senhora. No, senhora"—whichever she wants. Women with ideas she finds distressing, so you must have no ideas. Compreende?'

'Perfectly. But tell me, senhor. Are you in favour of taking a child's temperature every night?'

He shrugged charmingly. 'Who am I to say? What do I know of children? You must put that to my cousin.'

'Your cousin?' she echoed clearly.

A little too clearly, perhaps, for in the moment she began to speak the door had opened and someone came in. A tall man, this, in dark lounging trousers and a tailored smoking jacket, a wine-coloured cravat at his throat. He was quite different from Enrico, more alien about the dark eyes and brows, finer featured, far more arrogant and withdrawn. Linda's fingers curled on the arms of her chair. She had been mistaken, very much so. This was certainly the Marquez, and he was looking

16

at her as if he were accustomed to having people rise in his presence. Because she was a little dazed, Linda remained where she was.

The younger man said lightly, 'I have just met your Miss Grey, Luis. She tells me that she is not sure that my mother approves of her. You must set her at ease. Now that we have her here we certainly cannot afford to lose anyone so enchanting.'

'Remember that you are home again, Rico,' said the Marquez austerely. 'Your manners have suffered in Brazil. Leave us now, please.'

Enrico lifted his shoulders, flashed the ready smile at Linda and sauntered from the room. She eased slightly in her chair, wished it could have been true that Enrico was the Marquez. This man who was now seating himself behind the desk was even more ducal in his manner than she had expected, and he looked more than the thirty-five years Eve Bayes had given him.

He placed his hands on the desk, fine-fingered hands that looked strong as steel. He glanced at her from under those dark brows and his olive skin took up light on the high planes of his cheekbones as he leant forward.

'I apologise for my cousin,' he said formally. 'He returned unexpectedly yesterday from Brazil and will be staying here until he decides what to do. There will be no need for you to have further contact with him.' A pause, then, kindly, 'I am happy to welcome you here, Miss Grey. I believe you have already seen my aunt?'

'Yes, senhor.'

'She thinks you may be a little too young.' He appraised her calmly. 'I think so, too, but you come with excellent recommendation, and the small amount of Portuguese which may help you with my son. He knows some English from his former nurse, but I wish him to feel always that he can make you understand his needs.' He changed suddenly to Portuguese. 'Not many English girls would be willing to take a post in Portugal. What were your reasons, senhorita?'

She managed a fairly prompt reply. 'I wanted a change, senhor, and to see more of the world. I had seen only Oporto.'

Very faintly, he smiled. 'You had seen a great old city. Do you think you could be happy in the Valle das Flores?'

'I think almost anyone could be happy here.'

He reverted to English. 'You will get the pronunciation in

17

time, but it is not so important as that you should understand what is said to you by the child. English is a language which everyone should know, and Jacinto must grow up learning the two languages side by side, but we will talk about that later. His upbringing is at present in the hands of Doña Velira, and she will tell you what she requires. You have dealt before with children of his age?'

'Hundreds of them, senhor. Part of our training at Rawson Hall was a month here and there, in various children's homes. At the child guidance clinic we had to deal with individual cases and I think we met every possible problem, both psychological and medical.'

'We shall need only a fraction of your knowledge,' he said coolly, pleasantly. 'You must teach him, according to his age, and watch his health.'

With rather less assurance than she had tackled Enrico, she asked, 'Senhor, do you think it's right to take a child's temperature every night?'

He drew back in his chair, so that a faint shadow lay over his features. 'That, I believe, is the senhora's wish. You must do as she says.'

'But don't you agree that it's awfully bad for the child? A little boy shouldn't be reminded so often that health is a chancy business. If there's a suspicion that something may be wrong then naturally one takes the temperature, but normally just the back of the hand to the brow is enough, and even that can be done as if it's a caress, so that he doesn't suspect.'

The Marquez repeated, 'You must do as the senhora wishes. Far better to take the temperature too often than to risk an unforeseen chill.'

'I only thought,' she said, 'that if I'm with the child all the time I'll be bound to notice the first symptom.'

He stood up and moved round the edge of the desk, opened a box of cheroots and took one. 'With us, Miss Grey,' he said courteously, 'you will not have to take complete command of your charge. Chiefly, you will be his companion. For the rest you will act on instructions.'

Linda was roused, but dared not say more than, 'I'm sorry. I was thinking only from the child's angle.'

The finely-cut lips drew together, the chin lifted just slightly, as though at a faint challenge. 'Please wait until you quite understand what we shall demand of you before you voice objections. Perhaps this is the time for me to tell you what we shall expect of you, personally. You will have free time, of course, and there is no reason why you should not make some friends. You liked Mrs Bayes?'

'Very much indeed. It was thoughtful of you to send someone English to meet me.'

'It was fair, I thought. Mrs Bayes and her husband have been good friends of mine for some years, and I am sure she will like you to call on her when she is in residence in Merida. We do not wish you to be lonely.'

'I'm not the lonely type. I like walking and reading.'

He showed a faint surprise. 'Walking alone?' he queried.

'Why, yes. I enjoy companionship as well, naturally, but it isn't essential.' She waved a hand towards the darkness beyond the window. 'All this is quite strange to me, so I'll be happy for months, just exploring.'

'But here,' he said decisively, 'it is not usual for women to walk alone.'

'I shall just be one of the mad English,' said Linda. She saw a small change in his expression and added carefully, 'I'm afraid you're wondering if I was a wise choice, after all.'

'No,' he said, 'but I think you should realise at once that while you are with us you must behave as we do. A young Portuguese woman is never on friendly terms with any other man than her novio—fiancé, you understand? Perhaps she has a few good times with the friends of her brothers, but it is always in numbers, and there is never even a suggestion of intimacy.' He tapped the cheroot on the table but kept it between his fingers. 'In England, I suppose, you had many male friends?'

'One or two. No one close.'

'But you would go out with them, without a chaperon?'

'Well . . . yes.'

There seemed to be another fleeting change in his expression. It was odd for a man so cool and masterful, thought Linda, to allow the poker face to slip a little. But then he was a Latin.

His shoulders lifted in a shrug. 'While you are in England it is for your parents to decide. Here, I am your guardian, and I must impress upon you that I would not consent to conduct which in Portugal is indiscreet. If you are in doubt about this at any time you must come to me.'

'I see.'

'My frankness has vexed you?'

'Not at all, senhor. I'm in a strange country and willing to learn.'

He bowed, accepting her capitulation. 'I can see that you atone for the youthfulness with commonsense. Very British. On the whole, I do not interfere in the matter of Jacinto, but I do not wish you to think I am unapproachable where he is concerned. I would like that you regard yourself as a member of the household, with especially good feelings towards the Senhora de Filano.'

The insistence upon the importance of the senhora was beginning to rasp, but Linda smiled agreeably. 'I understand, senhor.'

'And I would like,' he added, with a hint of deliberation which was more subtle than emphasis, 'that you should not insist upon being very English. No change of any kind is possible here without my consent, and I assure you that I am not easily swayed. Jacinto is Portuguese; you cannot alter that, so please do not try.'

Linda was beginning to feel she had had enough. The senhora had seemed strict and hidebound, but in his way this man was worse. An aristocrat of the old school, ruling his castle and estate with an iron hand which was only thinly disguised by the velvet glove. The voice remained courteous, he even permitted himself to smile, but there was no mistaking his inflexibility. The wonder was that he had ever married and had a child.

She stood up and said politely, 'Is that all, senhor?'

His dark eyes flickered a glance over her fair colouring and slim shoulders. 'For the present, yes. Tonight I will write to your father of your arrival.'

'Oh, but it isn't really necessary. I shall be writing home myself.'

'It is nevertheless my duty to inform him that you have been received into this household. I trust you will be happy with us, Miss Grey.'

'Thank you,' she answered, and moved towards the door.

He took a long stride and placed his fingers on the handle, inclined his head. 'I am here in the library each evening at this time. If there should happen to be something about which you cannot consult the senhora I shall be at your service.'

Linda heard herself saying, 'But I'm rather afraid you'd turn down my suggestions.'

'Perhaps,' he agreed with the stern smile, 'but I have the feeling that you will try, all the same. Adeus, Miss Grey.'

'Adeus, senhor,' she said, a little despondently, and she went out.

For a moment she looked longingly at the great carved main door with its heavy bolts, then she turned and moved up the staircase towards her room. Well, that was over, and on the whole it had been no worse than she had expected. Different, but not more trying.

In England she had naturally wondered what the Marquez would be like, but she had not been able to form a picture of him. She had half remembered that the Portuguese were strict with their children, but had thought that a motherless little boy who was heir to a title might be spoiled. Not so Jacinto, it seemed—not with a father like that!

Linda crossed her room and passed between the curtains into the balcony. It was dark out there. A sky full of stars, a pale radiance over the lawns and trees, warm scents, the distant croaking of frogs, the faint clatter of crickets. A happiness spread through Linda's veins, and though she remained still her heart began to beat faster. This was what she had come for, this feeling in which peace was queerly blended with promise, the promise of enthrallment and a kind of bliss. She and the little boy would have good times together, and during her leisure hours she would read more about this country and find out everything about the Valle das Flores. In such a sun-soaked place it should be possible to find somewhere to bathe, and at the weekends there would be Mrs Bayes. What an age it seemed since she had parted from the woman in Portão!

The curtains moved behind her and a manservant said, 'Desculpe, senhora. The dinner is served.'

She thanked him and as soon as he had gone she inspected the folding table he had set up and the vast meal it held. A dish of chicken, another of diced beef with mushrooms, vegetables and salads, a silver plate piled with fruit, rolls and yellow curls of butter, cheese and coffee. She ate happily, took a long time over the milky-bloomed grapes. She poured coffee, reached for her bag and took out a cigarette. If smoking was on the forbidden list she didn't know it yet, so she could lean back and savour this particular cigarette. She wished her friends in England could see her now, but the wish soon passed, because she was back again in that room with the Marquez.

She couldn't make up her mind about the man. Superficially, of course, he was uncomplicated: the absolute ruler in his own world, cold and just, impossible of persuasion, and intolerant of men like his cousin, Enrico, who turned a pretty compliment rather too easily. But there must be another side to him, for he had loved and married. Perhaps tomorrow, when she made the acquaintance of Jacinto, she would get to know what sort of woman had invaded that fortress!

For today, Linda was already satiated with experience. Till bedtime she would read one of the exceptionally English novels she had brought with her, and relax completely. Upon which decision, she firmly erased from her mind the image of Luis Alvaro de Filano.

' CHAPTER TWO

THE new day was brilliant, and when Linda breakfasted in her balcony she made a discovery. Her room was at the side of the Palacio, and if she leaned far forward she could see the soft contours of the mountains, those same low mountains over which she had travelled yesterday, after leaving Portão.

This morning she had carefully chosen a darkish blue linen dress with a white collar and plain short sleeves, and as soon as she was ready she went downstairs and told the first servant she met that should she be needed she would be outside within view of the terrace. In reply, he informed her that it was unlikely that the senhora would rise before ten o'clock, and that a car would take her to a house in Merida to collect the child. Perhaps Miss Grey would not mind, he said, if he pointed out that it was usual to enter the grounds from the long sala, by way of one of the glass doors.

Linda didn't mind at all, of course. She entered the long sala, thought its magnificent carvings and murals rather excessive and gladly escaped into the hot morning sunshine. Today she was feeling much more herself; gay, open-hearted and more than ready for whatever might happen.

She walked some of the paths between the flowers beds, examined with sceptical eye some weathered statuary, and admired the pink waxen cups of the lilies on the pond. Now and then she saw a brown-uniformed servant passing along the terrace or across one of the lawns, but otherwise the great building, with its steeples and sculptures, its wrought-iron grilles and moulded balconies, dreamed away under the warm blue sky as it had done for centuries.

She sat on a stone bench under a tree and listened to the honey-bees in the branches. Presently a car came round the Palacio from the back, a surprisingly modern white continental affair with dashing lines and white tyres; but for the crest on the side and the fact that the Marquez was at the wheel, Linda would have connected the roadster with the debonair Enrico. She watched it disappear, and gave a relaxed sigh because the ogre was away for a while.

Not that the man's existence really bothered her much, or even awed her beyond normal. It was merely that with the

23

senhora up in her room and the man out of the way she felt free to linger and look at whatever she chose. She trailed along the wide terrace admiring the mosaic floor and the splendid columns of the arches, she found blossoms she had never seen before, and conjectured about the marble girl who was eternally washed by the fountain. It was while she was closing her eyes against the brilliance of the sun's rays on the cascading waters that the 'state limousine' came round the drive and Enrico got out.

This morning the idle young man was as entrancing as ever. His thick wavy hair, which was not nearly so dark as was usual in these parts, glinted red, and the mid-brown eyes had the lustre of dark topaz, while his smile would have endeared him for ever to almost any senhorita. In addition, instead of the normal sober garb of his class, he wore faultless green trousers and a brilliant sweater.

'Ah, good morning, Miss Grey. What an astonishment to see you here!'

'Is it?' she said unbelievingly.

'But of course! You wait for someone?'

'Only for the car. We're picking up the little boy this morning.'

'Oh, yes.' Linda was sure he overdid the long vowel occasionally. With him, 'yes' became an engaging 'yaze'. He added, 'Why should I not escort you to the house of my sister? It would be natural, no?'

'It might be natural, but it wouldn't be correct,' she told him firmly. 'I'll wait for the chauffeur.'

'But you trust me?' he demanded. 'What has Luis told you about me?'

'Nothing, except that you came back unexpectedly from Brazil.'

He shrugged, charmingly. 'Luis is the fast-and-hard over-lord. Me, I am a younger son with no money and expensive tastes. In Brazil, as you know, the Portuguese have many estates, and one of our uncles was sure he had emeralds on his land. I go there to help him find the emeralds, but all I find is red rock and a big boredom. So I come home.'

'And what are you going to do now?'

'Who knows?' he said lightly. 'Perhaps I shall stay and become a big business man. Quite certainly I could not settle here in Merida for ever. That is for men like Luis.' His smile sparkled. 'How was he with you last night?'

24

'Very kind.'

'The kindness which covers the ruthlessness. I am sure you prefer a man to be gentle and comprehending, as I am myself. Inside the kindness, Luis has a heart of stone.'

'Really?'

His hands went out. 'You do not believe me, but you will find it is true. He is so heartless that this morning he tell me I must not seek you out and flatter you! He would not believe that two people can see each other and afterwards see no one else.'

Linda couldn't help smiling. 'Did you try to *make* him believe?'

'What is the use? I always agree with Luis—just as I agree with my mother. How else would I live?'

'If you mean financially, you might try that big business you mentioned. I'm afraid you take the easy way out, senhor.'

He leaned forward and said softly, 'Rico, please, when we are alone. I have travelled and lost many of the old customs, and for that reason I am perhaps the only one here at the Palacio who will be ... simpatico to you. Already we are friends, is not?'

'Is not,' she replied. 'You're the cousin of my employer.'

'But you forget something,' he said winningly. 'I am the sheep of the dark family!'

She laughed, but didn't correct him. 'I think you should definitely find something to do.'

'Thank you, Miss Grey,' he said, and bowed. 'I am happy to tell you that it is found already. My mission in life will be to keep laughter in those amazing blue eyes.'

'Don't forget the Marquez' warning!'

Again the expressive shrug, the carefree smile. 'I did not seek you out this morning, and I certainly do not flatter you. Since you do not wish me to accompany you to the house of my sister I will not insist. Here is the chauffeur.'

He opened the back door of the car with a flourish, and she got in. The chauffeur took his place behind the wheel and the car began to move. Linda looked out into Enrico's laughing eyes, and smiled back at him. She supposed he was the typical younger son of a good Portuguese family, but he must be getting towards thirty, and to have reached such an age without an object in life he must also be lazy. Handsome and idle and addicted to snazzy outfits; the sheep of the dark family indeed!

But once they had passed between the stone pillars at the entrance to the drive Linda forgot Enrico de Filano. Because she was a little less of a stranger than yesterday the road looked familiar in this morning's translucence. There were the festoons of lemon-coloured flowers hanging over the wall, the many colours of the shrubs, the mulberry trees, and in the distance the green and pink and black tiled roofs of Merida. She saw donkeys led by peasant women, other women carrying baskets of flowers and vegetables on their heads, old men making rope by the wayside and children doing their stint in cottage gardens. The Palacio car was recognized, and drew bows and raised hats. The men, Linda noticed, lifted their battered headgear twice, once to the car itself and then to whoever might be travelling inside it. The deference was surprising and refreshing. Wonderful to be on the gilded side of the fence for a while!

They met the cobbled streets of Merida, and here there were more loaded donkeys and greetings, girls in the usual full black skirts with gaily striped aprons over them, and young men in cotton trousers and shirts, their brown skins firm and smooth, black hair rough and glistening.

They passed on into quieter avenues, and soon the car stopped outside a tall dwelling which was discreetly off-white with black-painted ironwork. The driver told Linda politely that there was no need for her to disturb herself, and he disappeared behind a thick dusty hedge, returning presently with the small boy and a plump and starchy-looking maid, who had seemingly been told she must herself put the child into the car.

Very quietly, and with self-possession, Jacinto took his place beside Linda and said goodbye to the maid. Then, as the car started off again, he turned and bade Linda a grave 'Bom dias, senhora'.

Something rather queer happened inside Linda. Possibly she had keyed herself up for the meeting with him, or it might have been the fact that at this first encounter he was so unchildlike that caused the odd little ache. With a half-smile she replied, 'Bom dias, Jacinto,' and for the moment left it there.

But as they went up out of the town she watched him. He lay back and looked out of the window, and she saw his small profile, perfect in the Latin fashion but too young to be determinate. His hair was straight and black and beautifully brushed, his suit dark grey, his shirt a startling white, his

26

small tie pale grey and immaculate. The toes of his black shoes he could have used as mirrors, and his slender little legs were encased to the knee in black socks. On such a day in England a child would wear sandals and shorts, perhaps not even a shirt.

But she had to admit to herself that the dress was not uncommon in Portugal. Even this morning she had seen two small brothers out with a servant, and both had been neatly dressed and well-behaved; they had held hands and walked sedately. Still, to Linda it was rather pitiable. She could think of no more heart-warming sight than that of a robust child, happily spent and grubby from playing in the open air. Fun and games in the bath, supper and a story before bed. Jacinto, she was sure, would have been quite bewildered at the very thought of such behaviour.

They were almost back at the Palacio when she said, 'I'm your new nurse. Did you expect me?'

His English must have been fairly good, because he answered, 'Yes, senhora, I knew you would come.'

'You must call me Linda.'

'Linda.' He pronounced in Portuguese fashion and looked at her. It seemed that he might make some comment about it, but his mind wandered. She saw him look at her face and hair, particularly her hair. The big dark pools of his eyes were unwavering till he had come to some conclusion, after which he saw that they were on the drive and coming to a halt.

In the terrace he took her hand automatically and walked with her into the sala. There he released the hand and walked straight across to the senhora, who sat sewing near one of the windows. He offered his forehead and stood back after the salutation.

'Bom dias, Tia Velira,' he said.

The old senhora spoke in Portuguese. 'How is it with you, my child? You have been happy with Tia Rosita?'

'Yes, Tia.'

'You sleep well?'

'Yes, Tia?'

The senhora was patently fond of him. 'Well, now we have the new nurse, Miss Grey, and we must teach her all the things she does not know about you. But not too fast, my little one.' She looked up and spoke to Linda. 'You will take Jacinto up to his bedroom and change his shoes, Miss Grey. Until eleven you will read to him from the big nursery book.

Then you will both have chocolate, which will be brought to you, and take a short walk in the gardens. At twelve-thirty Jacinto will have his lunch, and at one-thirty he will go to bed till three o'clock.'

'No walk after lunch, senhora?'

A patient shake of the head. 'It will be too hot. Go now. We will talk again later.'

Afterwards, Linda remembered that day as one of the longest she had ever waded through. A dozen times she was called down to the senhora and given instructions, and every effort to get under the child's polite exterior came to nothing. During the siesta hours she wrote to her father and Charlotte—a rather false little letter which made her new life sound wildly exciting. After his rest, the child had to be correctly clothed and walked once more in the grounds, and at five-thirty he ate his supper in the nursery. At a quarter past six he had to be taken downstairs to say goodnight. Linda watched the small boy approach his father, the absurd courtesy of his bow, the long, strong fingers momentarily on the little head.

'Boa tarde, Papa.'

'Boa tarde, pequeno.'

And that was all that passed between father and son. Linda couldn't understand it, but during the days which followed she began to realise that to the Portuguese there was nothing at all unusual in the relationship. From the cradle, Jacinto had been taught obedience, and silence in the company of his elders; he had learned that people of breeding do not shout or cry in public, that he, more than most little boys, had to be dignified in all circumstances. Quite certainly a child did not romp with his papa; in fact, he did not romp. Linda's first efforts at physical games were received with a wide-eyed stare.

His intelligence, fortunately, was above average, and he did occasionally enjoy the jokes she made as she read to him. But when he smiled it seemed to Linda like a challenge, and secretly she knew she wouldn't be satisfied till he let out a deep-chested chuckle; even then she would want him to keep it up.

On Sunday there was a luncheon party downstairs, and from her balcony Linda saw the guests walking about the garden. Men, mostly, but Eve Bayes was there with a man who looked so aggressively English that he must be her husband, and Linda hoped she would keep her promise to come up and see her. But instead she was summoned downstairs.

Mr and Mrs Bayes were in the small sala with the Marquez, and after Mr Bayes had been introduced, Eve said, 'Well, how goes it, my dear? Luis tells me you're settling down.'

'Yes, nicely, thanks.'

'I'd like to have seen Jacinto, but I understand he's sleeping.'

Linda nodded, too conscious of the tall dark man who stood with his back to the massive marble fireplace to be discursive. 'I think he's getting used to me.'

Mrs Bayes turned her bright glance. 'Jacinto is bound to like someone young, isn't he, Luis? Can you spare Miss Grey for my little party this evening?'

He said suavely, 'I did not know you were giving a party, my dear Eve.'

'It isn't the sort of affair that's in your line. There'll be Maria Barroz and her fiancé, the Gouveias, Rico and one or two others.'

'Perhaps,' said Luis with smiling indifference, 'it will be best for Miss Grey to become more accustomed to her surroundings before she meets others. There is plenty of time for making friends.'

'Well, let's fix it up for next Sunday,' said Eve, undaunted, as she turned back to Linda. 'After all, we English have to hobnob, don't we?'

Studiously cheerful, Linda answered, 'I'm all for it, of course. I shall be happy to accept your invitation.'

'You consent, Luis?' asked Eve casually.

Carefully, Linda queried, 'Is it necessary to have consent before I can go out during my leisure hours?'

He looked at her tolerantly. 'Everyone—even your country-woman, Mrs Bayes—accepts it. You must do the same. I will see that you are taken to the house of Mrs Bayes next Sunday at seven o'clock. The car will call for you at ten-thirty.'

Before Linda could make a reply which might be considered too British, Eve said smoothly, 'Then that's settled. I'll invite some young people for you, Linda, and we may bring some house guests with us from Portão. I'm so glad to have seen you today.'

It was dismissal of a kind, but Linda knew it was well meant. Eve Bayes had lived so long among these people that she was able to sense their reaction in any given situation. Apparently she knew Luis de Filano too well to allow any kind of development which might annoy him. Like everyone else, she would

29

move heaven and earth to stay on the right side of the Marquez.

Going back to her room, Linda fumed. That impossible man! No one dared do a thing without his knowledge and approval, and he took advantage of his power in every way he could. What reason could he have for denying her the pleasure of this evening with the Bayes? Why did he have to assert himself on so trifling an occasion? It was insufferable that one man should have so much power over many, and the worst of it was that no one else minded. Even Mrs Bayes took it gracefully for granted that Luis de Filano should have utter control of Linda Grey!

But it was not so much for herself that Linda minded. She had taken the post on his terms and would have to yield to him some of her independence, however, irksome it might be. But there was the little boy, living like a dummy in a well of luxury, hedged in by formality, permitted none of the fun that every child had a right to. If she could do nothing for herself, surely she could do something for him!

Gently, though! A new nurse had to feel her way into her employer's confidence; she already felt an affection for the lone little boy in the castle. She wondered sometimes what he had done about the inevitable emotional difficulties of his age. No mother, a tired old nurse, a great-aunt removed from him by about seventy years, a father who considered the child's up-bringing depended only on the integrity of the women who surrounded him. Jacinto had either had some bad times privately or been only half alive. Poor little sprig of the nobility!

Because he was becoming more and more important in her scheme of things, Linda learned caution. To the letter, she obeyed Doña Velira, but as far as she could she introduced more gaiety into the little boy's life. On their walks through the grounds she initiated him into the mysteries of hide-and-seek and lose-the-wand; she showed him how to fish in the pond with his hand and she put him on a low branch and swung him. Indoors, she looked in vain for the usual kinds of toys. There were a splendid rocking horse, a truly magnificent motor car and two gliders, but none of the shabby odds and ends to which children become attached. When Linda mentioned this to the senhora she received a typical reply.

'But Jacinto is now nearly four, Miss Grey. He begins to learn more serious things and grows away from toys. With all this training you have I think you know very little.' A shrug of the elegant shoulders. 'Here, we do not indulge our children and then grumble when they become young ruffians.'

The woman was impregnable, except where her younger son was concerned; for, much though she loved the child, she loved Enrico more. It probably never occurred to her that her beloved, disappointing Rico had had just such an education as the one she had decided upon for Jacinto.

Nightly, Linda watched the little boy as she took his temperature, nightly she vowed she would not do it again unless he appeared to need it. Invariably he looked anxious and said, 'Is it right?' To which she as often replied, 'It's perfect, darling. Just right.' But she hated the ritual.

Then one morning she had to come to a decision. It was as she looked through her wardrobe for a fresh dress and once more came upon her uniforms, sparkling fresh on their hangers. For a moment she was tempted to wear one of them and see what happened, but then it occurred to her that such an action might defeat her aim. Far better to do everything possible to please these people and ask her small favours at opportune moments.

But instead of wearing navy she winked at herself in the mirror and got into a brown dress she had once bought herself in a moment of aberration. It made her look mouselike and pale, not Linda Grey at all. After an hour or two in the frock she began to feel as colourless as she looked.

Mid-morning, Linda gave Jacinto his glass of chocolate, took him for his walk and examined with him a slumbering butterfly; but she could not forget the uniforms which gave her so much joy to wear. Rawson Hall had laid stress on the well-cut, slate-blue linens, and the design they had chosen was superbly right; slim-fitting, and just severe enough to impress the normal employer and give the child the feeling that his nurse was someone special—it was so important Jacinto should feel that way about his nurse. Perhaps it was through the lack of a smart uniform that the old nurse had been deemed drab and negligible, someone to be pensioned off when she grew querulous. At any rate, Linda knew she herself would never be happy here unless she could get into the beloved and familiar dress.

She would have to see the Marquez about it. The prospect was rather appalling, but now that her feelings about it had become urgent and crystallised she had no alternative. Tonight she would go to the library and state her case. If he insisted on informal dress she would intimate very politely that she would rather not stay. Hollowly, she knew that an ultimatum would leave him entirely cold, but she couldn't help it. For Jacinto, even more than for her own sense of security in this place, this was important.

She gave the boy his lunch in the nursery, played an energetic game with him to take the place of a walk after the meal, and sent him to bed. Being sent to bed was a novelty; he had been accustomed to standing still while someone else undid his buttons and sitting down while his shoes were taken off. Linda let him do these things himself, and he tackled them absorbedly, and climbed into bed in his pants and vest with a smile of accomplishment on his lips. Linda never fussed him in the daytime with lots of bedclothes; it was nice to lie there feeling sleepy with only a sheet over him.

Normally she read while he rested, but today she couldn't settle to a book. She had her own lunch, tidied her hair, and after telling the corridor maid to listen occasionally at the door of the young master's room, she went down into the grounds. It was quiet out there, the Palacio lunch-hour, and she drifted along one of the paths into an orchard where peaches were ripening and overblown apricots fell with dim thuds into the earth below. Like the rest of the estate, the orchard was trim and weedless, and she wondered if anyone here had ever had pleasure from those wild flowers which grew in such abundance all over the rest of the Valle das Flores. The Palacio was famous for its own sweet wine, made in the winery on the hillside, and for the rich cork from the forest beyond.

One day she would walk over to the cork forest. Today she must be satisfied with a stroll down to the lane used by the mule carts when they loaded hay and fruit. It was a wide lane and unsheltered, but Linda went on down the whole length of it to the gates, and passed a word with the man who had just opened them. She had gone less than a hundred yards back towards the Palacio when the white car came level and braked. She stood aside and gave a polite smile, expecting the Marquez to drive on, but he got out and bowed slightly.

'The unpredictable English,' he said pleasantly. 'Get inside the car, Miss Grey.'

'I like the heat,' she answered. 'I think my ancestors must have been warm-blooded.'

'So? That is interesting. You will nevertheless get into the car.'

What could she do but obey? She thought suddenly: this is my chance! And wished it had not been forced upon her so precipitately. She took her seat, he got back into the car and drove slowly up the lane.

'Senhor,' she said firmly, 'I'd like to speak to you some time soon about . . . one or two things. I intended coming to the library this evening. Will it be convenient?'

'Naturally. But I am here now. What is it?'

'One can't speak seriously in a car.'

He lifted his fingers from the wheel in a careless gesture. 'I would say it could be done. Jacinto is well?'

'Yes, senhor.'

'You, too, are well?'

'Yes, but . . .'

'Then there can be nothing so very grave that it cannot be spoken of now. What troubles you, Miss Grey?'

There was a note in his voice she had never heard before. The steel was still there but there was more of a lift to his tones. He was either in a good mood or mocking at her, and she couldn't imagine him mocking. Perhaps she ought to take advantage of the mood.

'We're nearly at the Palacio. I'm afraid I can't get it said that quickly.'

'No? I would have imagined that you could say what you felt very quickly indeed. But no matter. We will speak in the terrace.'

'But you're already late for lunch.'

He glanced at her, sideways. 'Is this problem of yours not more important than lunch?'

'To me, yes. But . . .'

'Then we will deal with it. Be still till we arrive, Miss Grey, and collect your arguments. You will need them all!'

She smiled vexedly, but was quiet. The wretched man had expected something like this. Having seen a spark or two in her eyes last Sunday when Eve Bayes had called, he had probably been surprised that she had waited so long before finding something else to complain about. He was cleverly one move ahead, but she was by no means defeated.

He drove round the fountain and stopped the car, took her up into the terrace and indicated a deeply upholstered chair. He hitched his trousers, took one of the ornate metal chairs and rested an arm on the round table. The lean face was half quizzical, half serious.

'Well, Miss Grey?'

It wasn't too easy, with him sitting slightly above her and giving her all his attention, but Linda was determined not to be intimidated merely by charm? Charm? She spared a moment to register the sensation; yes, he was being deliberately charming! How very odd.

She said resolutely, 'Senhor, it's about my uniform. Senhora de Filano told me the day I arrived that you don't wish me to wear one, but I believe you might understand my point of view rather better than the senhora. In the uniform I really feel what I am—a child's nurse. It gives me a sense of well-being and authority . . . and something else that isn't easy to describe.'

He glanced at the brown, tailored dress. 'Pride?' he suggested. 'You are anxious to flaunt this insignia of Rawson Hall?'

'Yes, but that's not the point. To be successful with children one must show both kindness and authority. If I appear to Jacinto as just another person I won't stand such a good chance.'

'A chance of what?' he asked gently, probingly.

'Of making him feel that he has someone of his own, someone different from the other people he knows. That's necessary to a child.'

'I grew up with a nurse who always wore the ordinary black,' he said. 'It made no difference.'

Linda hesitated, said quietly, 'No doubt you had a mother.'

His expression remained calm. 'That is so, but Jacinto has been given much affection and attention.'

'By someone young, who isn't a servant? I've only been here a week, but I've already noticed his needs. The senhora is too old . . .'

He said abruptly. 'No one could be more thoughtful and loving towards Jacinto than Doña Velira. She and I have many times discussed the way the child should be guided, so when you criticise the senhora you indirectly criticise me.'

She looked at him quickly, and away again. Criticism of the great man was obviously not permitted. She said, 'I really want only what's best for Jacinto. I happen to look ghastly in black, anyway, and most of my ordinary dresses aren't suitable for duty.'

'You regard your hours with the child as duty?'

The man was incomprehensible. How did he expect her to regard the job?

'An extremely pleasant one, senhor,' she said conventionally.

'I'm exceedingly fond of children, and Jacinto appeals to me very much. I want to do my utmost for him.'

'Very well,' he said coolly. 'Explain more fully.'

She paused. 'Well, a nurse glories in her uniform; it's like a badge of honour. Looking after children is one of the best careers any girl could wish for, and I've always been terribly grateful that my father gave me the chance of training at Rawson Hall. I'm really proud of it. Please believe that.'

'I believe it.'

'Then you understand how I feel. There's such a tremendous difference when a nurse in uniform bandages a cut knee and supervises the meals—the child himself is strongly conscious of it, and he trusts her and depends upon her when he's in doubt or unhappy. A little boy who . . . who hasn't anyone close to him learns about life from his nurse.'

His tones were perceptibly cooler and rather dry. 'I am afraid there is very little about Portuguese life that you could teach Jacinto.'

She said stoically, 'For a little boy growing up life is the same the world over; his chief needs are freedom and lots of love. If you insist that I may not wear the uniform, senhor . . .'

'I do not insist. It has been my habit to leave such things to Doña Velira, and I naturally wished to know everything from you before stating an opinion. There is just one thing which she may have taken into account, but which, it seems, has escaped you. She has an impressionable son under this roof and you are by no means unattractive.'

She coloured hotly. 'Good heavens! Can uniform make any difference? It's unbelievable that the senhora could think so!'

'But then, as I have mentioned before, you have not our ways, Miss Grey,' he said evenly. 'A Portuguese mother thinks continually of the health and happiness of her family, but she is also very much alive to certain dangers, and very conscious of the attractions of her own sons. There is a sweet girl whom Doña Velira has chosen for Enrico, and I daresay she feels it would be too bad if he were at this point infatutated with someone else.'

'It's too absurd to discuss!'

'You mean you could not in any way be drawn to Enrico?'

'Well, I . . . I suppose he has a certain something. He's adept at the compliment, and manages to look even more than he says. But he'd have to do more than that to make anyone fall in love with him.'

He smiled faintly. 'I like your occasional forthrightness, Miss Grey. It sounds to me that you see him often.'

'He's sometimes about when I take Jacinto for his walk. I know you don't care for me to speak to him, so I never linger.'

'That is considerate of you,' he said in the dry tones. Then: 'If it is so important to you and the child you may wear the uniform. What is the colour?'

'Blue, senhor.'

He looked narrowly once more at her dress. 'You had reasons for wearing this. You had already learned that I disliked seeing the former nurse in her brown suits which were so like those of my own menservants. However, I do not blame you. For your own sake I would say you should wear the uniform only in the mornings. If you wish to wear something pretty in the afternoons there will be no objection. I myself will tell Doña Velira.'

The sudden victory was almost too much for Linda. She glanced at him, saw the dark eyes go a little hard and knew it would be stupid to press her luck. Yet because she was Linda and Jacinto's welfare was close to her heart, she did so.

'I'm so glad you understand,' she said. 'Now that you've been so generous I hardly dare mention the other thing.'

His hand flexed slightly on the table. 'So there is something else?' he asked crisply. 'Is it perhaps that you should like to dress Jacinto in overalls and bright shirts!'

She smiled. 'Not at all. This is rather different. It's about that ever-present thermometer, senhor. Can't we put it away and use it only when it's necessary?'

'No!' A pause, then, 'This nightly taking of the temperature is something very important to the senhora and I see no harm in it. If it does not accord with this child psychology of yours you must make a game of it with Jacinto. That is the procedure for such things, I believe.'

'But it's too late. I think he must have known for a long time that the thermometer is connected with illness. Once a child has something firmly fixed in his mind you can't just laugh it off unless you drop the practice that started it. He always looks apprehensive till I've read the temperature and reassured him. And it happens every day, senhor!'

'I think you are making much of little, Miss Grey. It is up to you to devise some way of glossing those few moments while the temperature is being taken. That is all you wish to see me about?'

She nodded, and stood up as he stood. 'For the moment I'll keep quiet about the lack of fun in his life. It's a big subject.'

His smile was grim. 'I have seen him happy with you; it is enough. Tell me, Miss Grey—if I had insisted that you should not wear this famous Rawson Hall uniform, what would you have done?'

Her eyes, in the dimness of the terrace, were large and dark as violets as she contemplated him. 'Well, to be candid, I . . . I was ready to tell you that you must replace me as soon as possible.'

'That is what I thought. And now?'

'I'm very glad to stay. I'd have hated to leave Jacinto.'

'Then we are all satisfied?'

'Well, not quite,' she said reasonably. 'No girl could possibly be satisfied with knowing she is virtually a prisoner, and I'm not sure yet whether I shall get used to it or rebel.'

'You will become accustomed to it,' he said. 'That is another detail on which I insist.'

'I'll try. Thank you for giving me so much time.'

'It was a pleasure,' he said. 'You will now go to your room and rest.'

He opened one of the doors and they went into the cool tranquillity of the Palacio. At the foot of the staircase he bowed and left her. Linda mounted the stairs feeling a little odd.

It was some time later, when she had at last put down the book she had been trying to read, that she thought back almost word for word over that interview with Luis de Filano. Did the first small triumph mean that there might be others? Linda doubted it. For one thing, the senhora would inevitably guess that some understanding had been reached between Luis and the English nurse, and the knowledge was unlikely to please her. Next time, there would be a battle.

And had her success with the Marquez been so unqualified, after all? Obviously he hadn't cared whether or not she wore uniform; he probably considered it too small a matter for argument, for she was only the child's nurse. Yet he had the knack of making one feel necessary in the Palacio, whatever one's position. He was Portuguese, and presumably had some of the same tastes as his fellow countrymen. They all seemed to like their women in black, but it was seldom that a young woman wore it unrelieved. He was such a strong, vital sort of person that somehow she felt his taste in women might be rather unusual.

When Jacinto got up, Linda found herself looking at him for some trace of his mother. There must be a portrait somewhere and she determined to find it some day and study it; she knew intuitively that it would teach her a great deal about the child . . . and his father.

Yes, she admitted, she did want to know more about Luis de Filano. He gave the impression of always having been as he was now; arrogant and imperious, clever and strong, a shrewd, austere man with unexpected moments of lightness. But what of the younger Luis? Had he had some of that light-heartedness which was Enrico's stock-in-trade? Had he been more flexible and sparkling, interested in many things beyond the estate? Above all, had he been madly in love?

Attending to Jacinto in the bathroom, Linda chided herself. Her mind was wandering too far. That was what came of being shut away in a big stone palace with people who thought in another language!

That evening she made her own decision about the thermometer. She placed it well to the back of the top shelf of the massive bathroom cabinet, and when Jacinto reminded her that he had not had the pequena pipa under under his tongue she told him he was growing up and didn't need it so often; tonight, if he liked, he could use a cheese straw. This amused him because a cheese straw, if one nibbled it carefully, became a kind of cheroot.

CHAPTER THREE

LINDA wore the neat uniform, received glances but no comments. She had expected an acid remark from the senhora, or at least some small allusion to the matter, but her next meeting with the woman was no more of an ordeal than usual, and she came to the conclusion that Luis, as one would expect, was a first-rate diplomat. Somehow he must have omitted to tell his aunt of the interview on the terrace. He was capable of merely saying, 'We will let the English girl wear her uniform, Tia. She is young and needs it for the aid of command.' And leaving it there.

The rest of the week passed quietly. Linda was told she could be free from noon on both Saturdays and Sundays, but freedom, she found, was bounded by the estate walls unless she asked to be driven into Merida or to the mountains. She did go into Merida that Saturday afternoon, just as the town was awakening from siesta, and for half an hour, while the car waited in the market place, she walked the narrow cobbled streets with their lines of washing stretched overhead from window to opposite window, and looked over stable-type doors at an amazing conglomeration of local ware and eatables.

She came to a tavern with a terrace café, but didn't dare sit down because only men occupied the tables. There was a smaller café spilled all over a pavement, but again the only customers were men, to whom she was apparently quite intriguing. Portuguese women and girls, it seemed, simply did not go out with their menfolk. The few who went out without them never thought of asserting themselves to the extent of ordering a cup of coffee at a table and enjoying the passing scene. The day would come, Linda was sure, when she herself would ignore those young men who chatted for ever under the café awning, and really let herself go upon steaming chocolate and delectable pastries!

She saw the women selling their flowers and pies and vegetables in the market square, a dribbling fountain that was centuries old and used by everyone on wash-day. She saw stalls being heaped ready for the evening trade with crayfish claws, prawns, brown beans, tiny rusks, sausages and hard-boiled eggs stuffed with red paste. There was the usual smell of rich coffee mingling with the scent of flowers.

She would have liked to stay and watch the streets fill with people spending their usual Saturday night. Already an accordion was playing somewhere, and someone was singing a nostalgic folk song, one of those fados which are melancholy and not at all sweet, yet which pluck at the heart if you're a lover of Portugal.

But she had to return to the car, or the driver, she supposed, would grow restive. These Palacio servants were as strict as their master. She went back to the Palacio Filano and relieved the maid who sat with Jacinto. There was still tomorrow.

It was fun, the following evening, to dress up for the visit to the Bayes. She wore a navy blue dress with a tiny silver patterning on the stand-up collar, and stiletto-heeled shoes of the same shade. The child was already in bed and a servant sitting outside his door when Linda went downstairs into the hall, and tonight it felt like real freedom to go out of the big main door and step into the ceremonial limousine.

The house belonging to the English couple was on an avenida above the town, a Moorish style dwelling with a modern interior, set in about an acre of formal garden which was hedged in by clipped durantas and silver-leaved mimosas. In the bright light from the sitting-room windows Linda could see narrow paths dividing the lawn, a curly iron seat under a tree, and stars tangling with the topmost branches of a gigantic Cedar of Lebanon.

Eve greeted her warmly and led her inside to meet others. There were two dark women and two dark men, all four of them exceptionally agreeable; there was John Bayes with that truculently English nose of his and a welcoming smile. And there was Eve's brother, Michael Cullum.

'Mike's an architect,' Eve said. 'My young brother of thirty-one. He's been working very hard and needs a rest, so he's come over to spend a few weeks with us. I've told you about Linda, Mike. Does she look like home?'

Michael Cullum had a very pleasant slow smile. He was fairer than Eve, his hair almost sand-coloured, and he had a hazel glance which looked clear, but wasn't. In a dark suit he appeared slender, and there was a slight stoop at his shoulders, as if he had spent long periods at a desk. But no one would have dubbed him scholarly. In that first moment of meeting Linda thought him a rather appealing man with a chip on his shoulder.

He brought her a cocktail, sat down beside her and watched while she sipped with relish. He smiled. 'Long time have no drink?'

'Long time. I can have wine with my meals but I don't care for it except on special occasions. To be honest, I had a drink with my father the night before I left England, but it seems years ago.'

'A cocktail suits you. You're scintillating.'

'That's reaction. My days aren't dull, but they're unrelieved.' She set down her glass with a gesture that was very youthful, sighed happily. 'You know, it's wonderful to talk to someone English. Your sister was good enough to meet me when I arrived in Lisbon, but since then I've only spoken to her for five minutes, in the presence of my jailer.'

'Meaning Luis?'

'Oh, dear,' she said. 'Do you know him?'

'We met when I was over here two years ago. He was a bit stilted, but no more than you'd expect from a man in his position. Don't you get on with him?'

'One doesn't get on with the Marquez. One exists at his pleasure. I like him, in a way, but he gets my goat. However, this is my evening off. Tell me if England has changed at all since I left it a fortnight ago.'

He laughed and drained his glass, sat back and looked at her. 'England never changes,' he said, 'but I suppose Portugal is worse in that way. I always think of it as a country that stood still about two hundred years ago. That's what makes it so peaceful.'

'It's marvellous in some ways, but stultifying in others. After all, we English haven't stood still, but we have to live here as though we had. Your sister fits in remarkably well.'

'Eve's a little unusual. Being married to an Englishman she's not restricted, of course, so in Portuguese company she's able to behave as they expect her to without feeling the drag. What made you come here?'

'To Merida?' She paused, clasped her fingers about her glass. 'Superficially, it was because I was offered the job and knew a little Portuguese. Apparently it's unusual for a girl to have a smattering of any language but French, so I was snapped up. I think deep down I had a conviction that Portugal was strange and romantic.'

41

'So it is. The architecture alone is full of love.'

'The buildings are beautiful,' she admitted, 'but I don't believe I was thinking of stones and carvings, or even of the warmth and flowers. Frankly, I can't get close to the people at all.'

'Two weeks isn't long,' he reminded her. 'You need someone to take you about. Will I do?'

She gave him a smiling, critical glance. 'You might, but you don't live in Merida.'

'Would you take pity on me, if I did?'

'I'm not allowed to do anything without permission. At the moment I can stand it, but I don't know how long for. Tell me about your job.'

He did so, in low easy tones. He had recently designed a chapel and a school, but spoke as if all the enthusiasm he had expended on the tasks had left him without much appetite for further work. Now and then he looked tired and dispirited as he talked, and Linda reflected with some surprise that there must be more to architecture than she had thought.

She liked him, though, and had the pleasant feeling that he saw in her only a fairly likeable young woman. Unlike the Portuguese, he probably knew other fair girls with blue eyes, so that with Linda Grey he remained unimpressed. Which meant that they could be good companions without complications.

At dinner, she sat between Mike and a man named Pablo something, and she ate melon and fried chicken, ice cream and crystallised fruits. Because the two Portuguese women seldom spoke, except to be polite, she took care not to say too much herself, but it was good to listen to the men, to enjoy jokes she understood from John Bayes and Mike Cullum.

It was just as Eve was ready to announce that coffee would be served in the drawing-room that Linda's dark neighbour put a question.

'And what of Rico tonight? I have never known him to miss a dinner with the Senhora Bayes; he was a constant guest here before he went to Brazil. Is it possible that he is dining at the house of Juanita Montales?'

Eve hesitated, shrugged in a way which could convey almost anything in these parts. 'He may be with the Montales. I'm afraid I didn't invite him. We were already eight, and that's a good number, I find.'

In the general movement, Mike said to Linda, 'They're on

the matrimonial warpath with poor Rico, I understand. Eve was told she must not invite him here this evening.'

Linda smiled as if she understood, but inside she was just a wee bit angry. 'You know Rico, too?'

'As a matter of fact,' he said with a whimsical smile, 'he and I rather took to each other. Opposites, I suppose. He thinks himself no end of a chap because he gambles and drinks.'

'Was he like that? He seems to have sobered up since he returned from Brazil.'

'Really? I must meet him again. I was hoping to get him to Portão, so that we could go on the town together. I can do with a few binges.'

By now they were seated in easy chairs, all of them around the one low table, and talk became general. On the whole it was not an exciting evening, but the quiet conviviality relaxed Linda till she felt really happy and at peace. Towards ten Mike asked her if she would like to take a turn in the garden, a move which Eve felt called upon to explain to her other guests.

'In England, one does such things,' she said archly. 'Don't get notions about them, will you?'

Out in the fresh air Mike drew a deep breath. 'Yes, the starchiness does get you, doesn't it? I think Eve's worse than she used to be.'

'Perhaps she's just being wise.' Linda sniffed at a bush. 'Doesn't everything smell heavenly! I suppose being an architect you're a bit of an artist as well? Do you paint?'

'Only to wash in colour on a plan. I've no illusions.'

'Not about anything?'

'None at all.'

'That's sad. I've noticed that you look a bit hangdog sometimes. Yet you're a success, aren't you?'

He took her arm. 'I'm said to be.' After walking with her for a minute in silence, he added, 'You know, Linda, I feel I know you awfully well and you make me ache a little. You have a candid way with you that isn't nearly common enough among women. Perhaps it's because you're young and no one has yet torn any pieces off you.'

'You're not so aged. What happened?'

'Happened?' He had put up his guard. 'What do you mean?'

'Well, you're not too merry, are you? I'm not prying if it's

43

something private. I thought maybe you'd had a blow about some business proposition and might like to air it. On the other hand, you may be really tired and needing a holiday. It truly is a wonderful night. If you like, we'll just enjoy it, without talking.'

He was silent for so long that she thought he had taken her at her word. They sauntered slowly down the path and stood near the seat before turning back. But they had only taken a few paces before he stopped again, and detained her with a hand on her arm.

'I wasn't being offhand just now. Something did happen to me, and no one else knows about it. Eve said I looked worn but accepted my excuse of overwork. I decided I'd only get over it if I kept it to myself and tried to forget, but I reckoned without your keen eyesight. It was the sort of thing that often happens to a man like me. I had a girl and she married someone else—two months ago.'

'Oh, Mike,' she said quickly, softly, 'I'm so sorry. I honestly didn't think it was anything like that, or I wouldn't have . . .'

'That's all right.' He drew in his lip. 'I just went madly on with my job and got away as soon as I could.'

'And now, with nothing to do, you're getting the backwash. If you were so much in love, why didn't you hang on to her for all you were worth?'

'It wasn't like that. We weren't engaged, but I was working on something big and intended to ask her as soon as it was accepted. The good news came too late.'

'But it wouldn't have made any difference, would it, if she loved someone else.' Her voice rose, impassioned. 'It's too dreadful to think you can love someone without being loved back! I've always been so sure it was impossible. I do wish I could help you.'

He smiled. 'You're helping every minute. If I'd had your capacity for letting off steam I might have been over it by now. I'm glad I've told you, but don't tell anyone else, will you? Eve wouldn't understand.'

Linda was thoughtful. 'Knowing that life can be so mouldy makes one a little . . . apprehensive. Do you feel, now, that you'll get over it?'

'I shall have to.'

'Of course, and I expect you will. But is it still so new that recovery seems doubtful?'

He smiled. 'I'm somewhat older than you are, Linda, and in

the past two months I've become rather blasé. Even if I'd arrived here feeling I couldn't go on, I'd soon have changed, a bit. The Portuguese attitude to marriage is soothing, for one thing; and for another, I've met you.'

'Oh, but I . . .'

'Quite.' His glance at her was quizzical. 'I shan't make any mistakes about you, Linda, but merely to be near you is stimulating. Has anyone else ever told you that?'

'No, and I don't believe it. Why do you find the Portuguese attitude to marriage soothing? I'm afraid it irritates me.'

'The men make devoted husbands,' he pointed out.

'And the women excellent wives. But how can the two possibly know each other before marriage? They don't get a chance!'

'The way I feel now,' he said tolerantly, 'I'm all for it.' A pause. 'I hope I'm going to see you again soon.'

'Will you come to Merida next weekend with Eve?'

'Yes, but that's seven days away. Maybe I can work something out. There's a car arriving round the front. Will it be for you?'

'If it's exactly ten-thirty, yes,' she said with a sigh. 'I never knew a man like the Marquez for meticulously keeping his word. One of these days I'll break out—I know I will!'

'You're pretty enough to get what you want without having to fight for it,' Mike commented. 'Luis isn't made of cast iron, though Eve says he was different before his marriage—gayer and keen on sport. These days his thrills seem to be confined to fast cars and an occasional month of yachting at the sea.'

Eve came across the patio and called their names. 'The car's here, Linda, which means it's time for you to leave. I wish you could stay longer, but there it is. I've brought your stole and you can say goodnight to the others in the porch.'

'There can't be all that hurry,' said her brother. 'Surely there's time for a nightcap.'

'If you want Linda to come again she must go home punctually. In any case we ourselves have to leave soon for Portão. John has an appointment early in the morning.'

The chauffeur was standing beside the car on the drive, and before Mike could open the back door for Linda he himself had performed the courtesy. Mike repeated that he would see her again soon, Linda called another goodnight to the others and got into her seat. She sank back in the corner, waved a hand as the car moved off and in the same second became

45

aware that she was not alone.

'Rico!' she whispered, startled.

He smiled at her in the darkness. 'It is perfectly legal, my little mouse. The car first gathered me from the tomb in which live the Montales, and moved on to pick you up at ten-thirty. There was time for me to go home first, but instead I have been looking all alone at the moon.'

'There isn't any moon.'

'Which proves,' he said sadly, 'that I am in a dangerous state of health, for quite certainly I saw a large flat moon which had the features of Juanita Montales. I do not joke, Linda. This is a grave matter.'

'But it doesn't concern me.' She nodded warningly at the driver's back. 'Let's be conventional.'

'Do not worry about him—he is my friend, and he cannot understand much English, anyway. You have heard of these Montales?'

Linda decided that brevity might curb him. 'Yes.'

'You have also heard that my mother and Luis wish me to marry the daughter?'

'Yes.'

His hand lifted. 'Please. Not so abrupt. I am really in the jam and need to talk about it. The old Montales has no other children, so he has chosen me, because I am a de Filano, to be his son. I am to make love to a girl who puts ice in my veins, to be a model father and to learn about this glass goblet business of which he is the head, so that one day I may inherit his shares, which are considerable.' His shoulders lifted prodigiously. 'Needless to say, he is a man in his prime. I shall have many grey hairs and no ambition by the time I inherit.'

She laughed. 'You paint a depressing picture. I understood that Juanita is a sweet girl.'

'Perhaps,' he conceded, 'to anyone who does not have to marry her. I need someone with more fire and spirit, but unless I am helped by Luis I cannot afford to choose.'

'Are you in love?' she asked curiously.

'Only with you.'

'I mean the real thing. Is there someone else who might do?'

He took her hand firmly, would not allow her to withdraw. 'You will notice that I have told the chauffeur to drive round the town before taking the road to the Palacio. It was because

46

I must have a talk with you! But you speak as if you have contempt for me. I cannot endure it.'

'Loose my hand, Rico—and listen,' she said bluntly. 'You continually forget that I am an employee at the Palacio. I'm sorry they're trying to force you to marry someone you don't want, but it really hasn't anything to do with me. You must work it out for yourself.'

'Now I have vexed you! And I so much wanted your sympathy and assistance. Please be good enough to listen,' he begged. 'We have not much time, and this is something which I can no longer keep within myself.'

These men, she thought despairingly. But she answered, 'So long as you realise right now that I can't do more than listen. Go ahead.'

But Rico of the flashing eyes and impudence considered his words for once. 'Linda, have you ever wanted to do one thing more than anything else in the world? Have you ever been consumed by a desire for something which you could only obtain through other people? No, I think not—but that is how it is with me. In Brazil, I did not only dig for the elusive emerald; I also learned to fly. It was against my mother's wishes, so she does not know; neither does Luis, or anyone else in Merida. But to me it seems my whole future is in flying.'

'But it's wonderful!' she exclaimed. 'Isn't there an air line you could join?'

'A de Filano?' he said dejectedly. 'Luis could block my application. Also, it is not what I desire.' In his volatile way he changed his mood, leaned towards her eagerly. 'I have a friend in Lisbon who is also a pilot—an ace, you call it. Together, we have the plan to buy at first one plane and begin operations over the interior—freight and passengers, the small hops. Unfortunately, between us we can find only a few thousand escudos, and the cost of even a second-hand plane such as we need is considerable. So at present we are both the rolling stones growing much moss.'

'Poor Rico! It seems your only hope is the Marquez. Why haven't you consulted him?'

'To do that is to plunge into something from which there is no return. It is most distressing that I am the eye of the apple to my mother. She could not endure to think that I would fly.'

'But you're an expert, without her having known a thing about it! Once she's used to the idea she'll be proud of you.'

'Not Doña Velira! But though she is an obstacle most formidable, it is Luis who is the real opponent. Not only would he refuse to finance this venture for the sake of my mother, but he would oppose it for other reasons. Portugal, he would say, is not to be further spoiled by cheap tourism!'

'But tourists are a tremendous source of income everywhere. To be against them is to be entirely out of date. The Marquez uses modern methods in his farming, he's in big business. Give him a chance to understand.'

'How easy it sounds when you say it! What you do not realise is that at heart Luis is very Portuguese.' He added with a man-of-the-world loftiness, 'I have *worked* abroad, not merely travelled as a privileged visitor, like Luis. I have great understanding of people who are not so boxed-in by a strict code. Luis, I am afraid, does not approve of all I have learnt, and that is possibly why he agrees with my mother that I should settle down here as the husband of Juanita Montales. It is very depressing.'

'If you won't approach him, what else can you do?'

'I am in a tangle,' he confessed artlessly, 'but some things are very clear. The plan could not be financed without Luis.'

'Then consult him. I'm sure he'll be more sympathetic when he knows you're a qualified pilot.'

'It is possible that, to Luis, any young idiot could learn to fly and also get this idea of starting a small plane service. Ever since I returned to the Palacio I have known I must talk with him about it, and now that I am welcomed by the Montales family it becomes urgent. I cannot let that go too far.'

Linda looked out of the window and saw that at last they were leaving the town. Though the sky was dark, she saw it brilliant for a moment, with a plane coming in to land somewhere along the Valle das Flores; she saw tourists descending, but not many of them. A pensão or two would take care of the few who might wish to remain overnight. Unless it was turned into an industry tourism didn't really spoil places, though she wouldn't like to undertake the task of convincing Luis de Filano of that fact.

She said casually, 'Someone told me only tonight that the Marquez was quite different before his marriage. Was his wife . . . beautiful?'

'Amalia?' Rico considered this. 'Yes, she had beauty of the fragile kind.'

'Is Jacinto like her?'

'No, I think not. He is just a menino without much likeness to anyone so far.'

Linda's throat was oddly dry when she put the next question. 'Were they terribly in love—Luis and his wife?'

To Rico, it was the sort of question one might expect from the quaint English. 'A man like Luis,' he informed her very kindly, 'does not fall terribly in love. Amalia was the daughter of a visconde who lives in Portão, and from their early years she and Luis were more or less betrothed. She was gentle and quiet, not very strong. Most of the time they were married she had to spend at her father's villa near the sea. If Luis is changed, it may be that he realises marriage was not for him. Certainly he has given himself almost entirely to the estate during these last years.'

The picture he gave was very like the one Linda had formed for herself. Not only was Amalia's portrait missing from the Palacio gallery but there seemed to be no evidence whatever of her residence there. She had altered nothing, initiated nothing; had simply floated like a wraith within the rooms and corridors for a year or so, and vanished, leaving hardly a trace of herself, even in Jacinto.

It was strange to think of Luis marrying such a woman. He would have taken the utmost care of her, of course, and been very tender with her because that was his way with people who belonged to him. But what a strange marriage for a man so strong and virile!

Rico was saying, 'This rigid way of life which Luis prefers is difficult for us who are not so minded. On my way home from Brazil I had no doubt that I would tackle him, but here I am back in the meshes of it all, with the addition of a prospective father-in-law whose only wish is to trap someone into his glass factory! It is too bad, this! I cannot support it.'

'Then you'll have to do something about it, won't you?' said Linda equably. She indicated the spread of the Palacio against the night sky. 'The senhor may be right, you know. It would be an awful pity to destroy this atmosphere. On the other hand, it might help considerably to have more of the larger towns linked up by air. You must certainly speak to him about it, Rico.'

'So you are of the same mind as I?' he said quickly, with mounting excitement. 'Luis must be stormed, and at once. But will I have the courage to do it alone?'

'You could bring along your friend the pilot.'

49

'Oh, no. He is the type to blunder. I think I am also the type to blunder, and that is why . . .' The car stopped and before she could move he had again grabbed her hand. 'Linda, I beg of you—go with me to Luis! I do not ask you to speak unless it is necessary, but lend me your support.'

'I can't possibly do that. My opinion wouldn't carry weight, anyway, and Luis would only be angry that you should have dragged me into it. See him alone, Rico, and be frank with him. That's all you can do.'

'And if he is not sympathetic?'

'You will have to think of something else.'

He bent and kissed the hand he held. 'You are so sane, my little blue-eyes. I am afraid that if I do not succeed I shall come back to you. I am definitely falling in love with you.'

'Then you'll definitely stop right now. We must go in, Rico.'

The big main door yielded, and they entered the vast quietness of the reception hall. Rico walked with her to the foot of the stairs, detained her with a touch on her arm. In the light he was extraordinarily handsome and appealing, and those red lights in his hair gave him a deceptive look of power. In the brown eyes were entreaty and something which had the disturbing appearance of love. For just a second it occurred to Linda that it might be easy to return his love; but only for a second. There was no magnetism between them.

Her glance was drawn swiftly to an opening door. Before she could warn Rico he had taken both her hands and was raising them to his lips.

Luis came forward, looked from one to the other. Very coolly he said, 'You have had an agreeable evening, Miss Grey?'

Rico straightened and turned. Linda nodded.

'Yes, thank you. Goodnight, senhores.'

Without haste, she began to mount the staircase. She heard both men answer her.

And she heard Luis say stonily in Portuguese to Rico, 'I was hoping you would arrive home earlier because I wished to speak to you on an important matter. Come with me now into the library.'

Linda went on, along the corridors and into her room. Quietly, she looked in upon the sleeping child, and because she did not want to stop and think she began to get ready for bed.

On the whole it had been an exhausting evening. It had started off peacefully enough, but she had always found that other people's misery or troubles took a great deal out of her. There had been Mike Cullum and his unhappy love affair, which really had been plenty for one evening. But right on top of it Rico had unloaded his seemingly insoluble problem, and though she had tried to remain aloof from it, she hadn't been able to avoid showing him that she was on his side. After all, the fact that he had trained to fly signified enthusiasm; having often been an enthusiast in some direction herself she felt a slight bond with him, but that was all. She refused to be mixed up in the business.

But as she became drowsy, a little later, she forgot both Mike and Rico. She thought of the frail Amalia living away near the sea while Luis ran the estate, and wondered why the knowledge gave a lift to her heart.

At nine o'clock next morning a maid came with a message.

'The Senhor Marquez wishes to see you in the small sala, Miss Grey. I am to stay with the senhorito till you return.'

Linda's hands went a little damp, she unnecessarily straightened the plain white collar of her uniform and smoothed the cornsilk hair. Rico last night, herself this morning. Oh well, like a visit to the dentist it had to be gone through. At the worst, she told herself once more, he could only kick her out.

She knocked at the door of the small sala and obeyed his command to enter. Luis closed the door and indicated one of the ornate chairs.

'Good morning, Miss Grey. I will not keep you long.'

She stole a glance at him, saw him very dark and tall, and expressionless except for the slightly indrawn lip which in anyone else might mean indecision. In the Marquez it was more likely to denote preoccupation with some problem more weighty than the one now being dealt with. The pale grey suit enhanced the width of his shoulders, and Linda found herself looking at him in the light of the new scrap of information gleaned from Mike. Yes, one could imagine him trimming a yacht against the wind or fanatically speeding in a high-powered car. For some reason the small ache in the region of her heart once more became noticeable. Queerly, she reflected that might be better if he did dismiss her.

It seemed there was nothing of that kind in his mind. He

said flatly, 'My cousin told me last night about this scheme of his. He thought it important to impress upon me that you are in favour of it. Why should he do that?'

Linda hesitated. 'Didn't he give any reason?'

'Oh, yes,' with irony, 'Rico always has a reason. I would like to compare it with your explanation.'

'There's nothing to explain. He told me he'd learned to fly and wanted to start a small service here in Portugal; he said you'd be against it, but I pointed out what he already knew— that whatever happened he had to consult you about it. There was nothing more.'

'You did not advise him to end his connection with the Montales?'

'No. How could I?'

'Yet he is doing so—or proposes it,' said Luis sharply, 'because he considers himself in love with you! I have never heard anything so utterly absurd.'

Linda's blue glance flashed up at him. 'That's hardly complimentary, senhor! I may be only a minor member of your staff . . .'

'It is absurd,' broke in Luis, 'because the basis of it is childish. You are in favour of his plan and therefore he loves you! With Senhor Montales he would have to work himself into a good position and strive to be worthy of an old and famous business, but he cannot contemplate so much effort. He would rather own a plane and give his mother nightmares.'

'All pilots have mothers or wives, very often both. Women have always done a tremendous amount of waiting and worrying, and for that reason one can't blame Rico . . .' she paused imperceptibly, annoyed that she should have used the pet name, but carried on, '. . . for his attitude where his mother is concerned. The senhora will perhaps have to face the fact that he's not the type to settle here and be happy.'

The dark eyes narrowed. 'You seem to have learned a great deal about him in a short time.'

'To me,' she said politely, 'he's fairly transparent.'

'And to him, you are the angel who will intercede for him! I called you in here this morning to tell you not to waste your time concocting a method of approach. I have said all I wish to say on the subject.'

'Very well, senhor. May I go?'

'No.' He walked to a window and looked out, so that she saw the distinguished profile, the hard line of his jaw. Without turning his head, he asked, 'How does it feel—this inspiring of love in a man in so short a time? It is something you have not experienced before, no?'

'I don't think it's happened now,' she said evenly.

'We cannot be sure—but if it had? Would it excite you?'

'Perhaps, if it were real.'

'Even if you did not return the love?'

'Possibly. After all, it must be rather exhilarating to be loved.'

A brief silence. Then: 'Your name is Linda, is it not? We have the word linda in Portuguese. It means fine and beautiful.'

'Yes, I know. I didn't remember the word but Jacinto told me one day.'

'To say such things the boy must care for you already.'

Linda nodded. 'I think he does. Loving can happen very quickly with a child; it's more instinctive. If I left him he'd soon forget me, too.'

'You leave the doors wide open, Miss Grey,' he said, as he turned her way. 'You would not have me think you are becoming indispensable here.'

'No, I wouldn't,' she returned quietly.

'Why? Are you perhaps a little afraid?'

For an instant she met his glance. 'Afraid of what?'

A shrug. 'Of yourself, maybe. You are not the typical children's nurse, and you are young, besides. Do you feel that you may miss a great deal if you stay with us too long?'

'You mean,' she asked candidly, 'that I may chafe against being imprisoned?'

He smiled faintly. 'Not exactly. I was remembering that we have not the same things available here that you have in England. There you have cinemas and cabarets, which you attend with any man who cares to invite you; you dance with anyone. It follows that there are other things—little things which pleasantly inflame the emotions. Naturally you will miss them.'

Feeling more at ease, Linda said demurely, 'But those are things one knows. Here there can be adventure even in a glance, if one is so minded; romance is comparatively safe.'

'Yet with Rico,' he said, an experimental inflection in his tones, 'you have gone beyond the glance. He tells you his dreams and you enter into his plans. Is that still harmless romance?'

'It's harmless and not romance. As a matter of fact,' she said as non-committally as she was able, 'I wouldn't want the Portuguese type of love.'

He did something that she knew was not characteristic; he plunged a hand deep into his pocket and kept it there. 'And what,' he asked evenly, 'is wrong with the Portuguese type of love? Can you speak from knowledge of it?'

'No, only from observation and what I've heard. Your cousin is a case in point. It seems he is expected to fall in love with Juanita in order to inherit her father's glass factory.'

His nostrils thinned. 'Rico is not a good example. In everything he has always been unstable. One tries to guide him for his own good.'

'But can it be right to tell a man of his age whom he shall marry—particularly when he's not too keen to marry at all? Your arranged marriages seem to be fairly happy, but there must be some people who simply fall in love—just an exception to your golden rule, here and there. What happens to them?'

'We are arriving nowhere, Miss Grey,' he said coolly. 'I accept that you do not care for our customs, but once again I must ask you to respect them. So that you will not be able to encourage Rico in this notion of his I have arranged for him to stay with his sister in Merida.'

She was stung to retort, 'I only listened to his plans; I didn't suggest them! But since we've come back to them, may I ask something? Apart from the effect on Doña Velira, what are your objections to the starting of a small air service inside Portugal?'

'One cannot rely on Rico—therefore the objections are many.'

'But that's not all, is it? You don't want the outside world brought any closer to your beloved countryside, do you? You are the feudal master of the Valle das Flores, and progress could interfere . . .'

'You will be quiet, Miss Grey!'

The thread of fire in his voice stilled her. She drew a breath, relaxed her tight hands. Heavens, what had got into her? She didn't feel as strongly as all that about Rico and his dreams. The trouble was that when the Marquez was in a certain mood it struck a spark within herself and she was tempted to let out the most unwise remarks. She stood up.

'I apologise, senhor.'

But his eyes still glittered. 'Once you have said a thing like that it is too late to be sorry!'

'I suppose you're wondering whether I'm good for Jacinto?'

'You are good for Jacinto,' he said rapidly, 'but you are not very good for others, including yourself! I forbid you to speak to anyone ... *anyone*, you understand! ... on this subject. And you are to have no communication with Rico.'

Small hairs rose on the back of Linda's neck, but she kept control of her tones. 'I'll do my best to obey, senhor. In time I shall probably get used to tyranny.'

The silence which followed was electric. Luis had come forward and the gleam in the dark eyes changed to a blaze. For a long moment Linda nerved herself for some kind of violence; it was there, quivering between them.

Then the door at the end of the room opened and Doña Velira came in, preceded by her maid, Lupe. The maid curtsied to the Marquez, placed a chair in the senhora's favourite position and drew up a footstool.

The senhora accepted the attentions graciously. 'You may go, Lupe.' She leaned back in the chair, making herself comfortable, looked up at her nephew as he bent conventionally over her hand. 'Good morning, Luis. It seems you have had occasion to speak to Miss Grey.'

'On a small matter,' he conceded in normal tones. 'You are well this morning, Tia Velira?'

'Thank you, yes. I was going to call Miss Grey myself. It is our little one's birthday on Thursday, as you know, and now that he is four it will be necessary to start one or two organised lessons. What do you suggest, Luis?'

His shoulders lifted and he moved a pace towards the door. 'Miss Grey has been trained in these things. She will know.'

'Very well. She and I will arrange it together.'

The senhora again adjusted herself in the high-backed chair, and as Luis did not make any further movement, Linda rather numbly put a question.

'Do we have some celebration for Jacinto's birthday?'

'He has some new toys,' said the senhora, 'and a special cake at lunch time.'

With a trace of sarcasm, Luis said, 'Does that meet with your approval, Miss Grey?'

Almost recovered now, she answered, 'Whatever you wish, senhor.'

He said indifferently, 'I must ask you both to excuse me

now. I am expecting old Gonzalez here, to do my accounts, and I wish to settle him with the books myself.' He bowed and crossed to the door, paused there and turned. In cool, aloof accents he said, 'I feel Jacinto is now old enough to take one meal each day with us downstairs. You will rearrange his day, Miss Grey, and come down with him for lunch at one-thirty, commencing on Thursday.'

The senhora looked from under her hooded lids at the pale-skinned English girl, and then at the Marquez. 'You wish Miss Grey also to lunch with us, Luis?'

'It is necessary, I think,' he said. 'The child will have to be watched.' And he went out.

The senhora sat very still. And Linda waited.

CHAPTER FOUR

SENHORA DE FILANO was not deliberately destructive; Linda had realised that from the beginning. She merely lived according to an accepted list of conventions and was far too set in the code to change in the least. She knew that in England and elsewhere a child was allowed to express himself, but she would point out that such children made no better men and they made far worse adolescents than those existing in Portugal. Where she was most obtuse was in her understanding of the child mind. To Linda it seemed that the senhora just didn't believe that the child mind existed; she thought there was only one type of mind and that children simply had to be taught how to use it.

But the senhora's thoughts were not at that moment entirely upon Jacinto. She left Linda standing there near the low table, looked up at her, and asked, 'There was some trouble between you and the Marquez this morning?'

'No trouble, senhora,' Linda replied politely.

'He looked angry when I came in, and afterwards I thought his tone was strange. Did he reprimand you?'

'Yes.'

'You do not take kindly to such treatment?'

'I daresay it was deserved, senhora.'

'Luis is very just. If you wish to stay you must try to please him. Certainly you should not look as you did when he asked if you approved of the little celebration for Jacinto.'

'The senhor knew I didn't approve—even before he asked.'

Doña Velira absorbed this, pressed together the tips of her thin white fingers and bent her head forward a little, so that with the light behind her she looked like a hawk carved from bone. 'And why do you not approve, Miss Grey?'

This was easy. 'Children have one day a year that's all their own—their birthday. It's an exciting day because it begins a new year and to the small mind has immense possibilities. Also, for that one day in the year he's really important and feels older, and it's good for a child to know he's important occasionally. Jacinto is old enough to enjoy a birthday party.'

'There are few children of his age among our friends, and by virtue of our position here we are to a great extent cut off, but he is not lonely.'

'He doesn't have any fun.'

'He is not unhappy.'

Linda knew it was no use getting heated with the senhora; in any case, she felt she had done enough in that line for one morning. So she said patiently, 'You say he's not lonely, he's not unhappy. That's true, but the condition is negative. He should be carefree and bubbling with joy, getting into scrapes. If I had a free hand I'd make him that way.'

'Then it is as well that you have not a free hand. We do not want a little . . . hooligan in our midst! You would ruin the child with continual play.'

'He's only four, senhora, and the years of childhood are so very short. A child learns and becomes strong by play. Jacinto should have a sandpit in the garden, a swing, a see-saw, some baby tools. . . .'

'You have said all this before, Miss Grey. I do not wish to hear it again. Let us get down to this business of lessons for the pequeno. You will need books.'

Linda quelled a sigh. 'To start with, he has enough books. He needs more bricks—shaped ones of all sizes and colours. A small paint box and some chalks and crayons. A tea-set . . .'

'You would make of him a girl!'

'Little boys are as keen on dramatics as little girls; they don't take to exclusively boyish things till they're older.'

'But these things you mention are still more toys!'

'They're toys that teach, senhora,' said Linda a little wearily. 'A child who plays well is healthier and happier than one who's kept inactive and lonely. Swinging and climbing develop the muscles; with the aid of bricks you teach letters and figures and colours, small additions and subtractions; you train the senses with puzzles and toys that fit together. A child who learns while he plays and goes to bed happily worn out is not likely to be frustrated.'

'You quote from your text books, Miss Grey,' said the senhora coldly. 'I am not interested. I will myself procure the books from which I wish him to learn.'

'Is there no child at all with whom he can play?'

'There is no child with whom we wish him to play, Miss Grey. I believe you yourself play with him a great deal.'

'But it isn't the same. Play is normally a serious business to children and they play best when they have another child with them. An only child . . .'

'We will not go into that. Jacinto has to be alone. When my nephew marries . . .' The senhora stopped as if she realized that this was only Miss Grey, the child's nurse, to whom she was speaking. She ended, 'I will attend to the matter of those books. And please let me have the list of clothing replacements, so that it may all be accomplished on one visit to Portão.'

Linda murmured something and went from the room. She thanked heaven for the stairs which she could mount two at a time to gain a measure of release. Doña Velira was the most deflating woman she had ever met, and a session with her always took some getting over. Following the interview with the Marquez, this morning's dose had been even less palatable than usual, and Linda rather wondered at herself for putting up with it.

Much of the unpleasantness was her own fault, of course. Another girl in her position would not become vexed and exasperated at every vetoed suggestion as she did herself. Anyone else would shrug and let these people have their way with their own child, relax and enjoy the good food and rich bedroom, the salary, the alien atmosphere. Linda Grey was stupid, she decided, and she wished she knew what she could do about it.

She sent the maid away and crossed the nursery to see what Jacinto was doing. He merely sat at the child's table with his arms crossed upon its surface, and stared down over the balcony at the grounds, but as he became aware of her he looked up and smiled.

'I watch the birds,' he said. 'They eat the flowers in the bushes.'

'Naughty birds—but there are plenty of flowers.' She lowered herself to one of the small chairs. 'Did you know it's your birthday three days from now—Thursday?'

'Yes, I remember. I have four years now.'

'That's quite a big boy. Did you have a happy birthday when you were three?'

'Very happy,' he said gravely, but there was a blankness in his glance which meant that he was only being polite. Because the day had been like any other he couldn't recall it.

Linda wrinkled her nose at him, and leaned closer. 'Jacinto, what would you most like for your birthday?'

He had to think that over, with his chin in his hand. 'Another engine?' he said at last, obligingly.

'All right, another engine. Now think properly and tell me what you'd *really* like, if you could have it.'

He thought, and shook his head. 'Perhaps a book.'

'Is there nothing you *want*?'

'You tell me,' he said, and wriggled in readiness to enjoy whatever might come.

Linda pretended to think very hard. 'A tricycle?'

He answered slowly, 'Not a tricycle. Tia would not let me have it.'

'Would you have it if you could?'

'Perhaps.'

'A golliwog?'

'No.'

'A bat and ball?'

'I would like that, yes.'

'A puppy?' said Linda, a little breathless herself now that she had reached her objective.

His big dark eyes stared at her, almost mirroring the small heaven he was seeing. 'But that's alive,' he breathed. 'I could not have for a gift something that lives.'

'You might. We'll ask Papa—write him a little note. You may not get it, but we can ask.'

'He will say no,' said Jacinto with conviction. 'There are dogs at the porter's cottage which belong to Papa, but we do not have them indoors.'

'We'll write the note anyway. Stay here while I get some paper and an envelope.'

They wrote the request in Portuguese, Linda holding the little boy's hand and shaping the letters as childishly as she could.

'Dear Papa, May I please have a puppy for my birthday? I will not mind having no other presents, but I would so like a puppy for my very own, so that I can teach him tricks and watch him grow. He would be my little friend. Please, Papa. Your affectionate Jacinto.'

As she sealed the piece of paper into the envelope Linda felt odd, and very defiant. If they wouldn't let Jacinto play with other children they must just provide a substitute! The few lines, a special plea from Jacinto himself, were likely to be regarded as a form of blackmail, but Linda was sure that Luis would hate the child to feel he was being denied something he badly wanted. Jacinto, through his upbringing, had never

60

before been young enough in his ways to demand the things he had a right to. It was about time he acted his age!

Soon after eleven, she took the child for his walk, and Jacinto gave the letter to a servant and asked him to see that it reached the Marquez.

'There! Now we have to wait and see what happens,' Linda said.

For one so young his expression was sceptical. 'Papa will tear it up,' he told her. 'Perhaps Tia will say it was bad manners.'

Linda hoped Tia wouldn't know anything about it. She knew that if the request displeased Luis he would not blame the boy; he would chalk up another mark against Miss Grey. Well, let him! If, in the old nurse and the new, he still could not find one whom he considered suitable for his child, he should marry and let a woman manage things for him. The old senhora had spoken of the possibility of his marrying; in fact, if Linda remembered rightly, Doña Velira had said, '*When* my nephew marries . . .' as if there were already a prospective bride on the horizon!

This new conception of Luis was disturbing. Linda suddenly remembered a comment she had heard from one of the Portuguese at Eve Bayes' the other night: 'They say Nolette del Carros will soon be returning to Merida after her years of study in Lisbon and elsewhere. She went away an eager young woman and she returns a sculptress of some note. She will have changed, but not, I think, towards the Palacio.'

For Palacio, thought Linda soberly, read Luis. Well, perhaps for Jacinto that was the answer, because only if Luis married again would Doña Velira be displaced as the boy's guide and disciplinarian. It didn't really matter if it were this Nolette del Carros or someone else.

Not that a change seemed to be imminent. Surmise and conjecture didn't make a thing true, and putting two and two together as she was doing now was apt to be depressing. But like sugar under the shoe, the statement which Doña Velira had begun and left trailing grated every now and then, and Linda couldn't think why.

It wouldn't worry her terribly to lose her job, and she had been dealing for too long with the young to care more for Jacinto than for anyone else's child. No, that wasn't true. There was something special about Jacinto; he was alone, and a little sad in his riches, his need for the ordinary things which kept poor children happy as larks. She found it comforting and touching when his hand slipped into hers, or when he asked politely if he might please come to her room while she changed her shoes or tidied her hair. He was arriving late at the small independent actions, but the sight of him strapping his own sandals and buttoning his shirt with intense absorption caught at her heart. She was sure the arrogant Luis had never been such a retiring little boy, for all his governess in black!

No, Jacinto would always be a quiet child; intelligent, but rather diffident. It was painful to imagine him with a step-mother who might injure his feelings, or with one who gushed and didn't understand him. The motherless child was par-ticularly vulnerable. But what could Linda Grey do about it?

A letter from her father arrived that afternoon. He had heard from the Marquez and answered his letter, and both he and Charlotte had laughed at the thought of her incarceration in a Portuguese castle. The lighthearted Linda, of all people, to find herself in a spot where she couldn't even go dancing with a nice man now and then! What in the world did she do for light relief?

Linda slipped the letter into a drawer. She couldn't see any-thing funny in her situation, and neither could she remember very clearly the person she had been in England. At the moment Portugal was more real; it claimed all her attention.

When she tucked Jacinto into bed that night she realised that not another word had been said about the puppy. He wasn't crossing his fingers, as some children might; he just didn't believe in miracles. Perhaps it was as well, she thought. The sort of miracles that most children were willing to credit didn't happen at the Palacio Filano.

The next two days passed tranquilly, except that Rico came to visit his mother and tossed a flower up into Linda's bal-cony as he left; which indicated, she supposed, that he bore her no ill-will for advising him to consult Luis.

Jacinto's birthday dawned like any other morning. There was soft pearly sunshine, the early coolness from the moun-tains, scents from the flowerbeds. Linda got up soon after six, put on her blue wrap and went into his room. The child lay awake, staring dreamily at the moulded angels on the ceiling. She bent over and kissed his forehead.

'Happy birthday, darling. Do you want to get up?'

'Is it time?'

'Don't you want to be different this morning? How would you like to run into the garden and pick some flowers?'

He sat up straight. 'Do we have Tia's permission?'

'No one will know, except perhaps the servants. Come—pop on your dressing gown and slippers. We'll find a bouquet for the nursery.'

He was anxious but trusting. He belted the dressing gown, looked at the edges of Linda's pyjamas below the flowing robe and actually giggled. In the corridor his fingers tightened about hers and he made no sound as he walked with her right to the end and down the back stairs. They met old Josef in his green baize apron, but a finger to the lips made him a conspirator. He nodded and smiled, perhaps remembering days when he himself had loved the feel of the morning, the clean perfume of dew on the grass. He opened the door for them, and they went out into a wash of pure sunshine which sparkled over the the dew and lent a pristine loveliness to the magnolia and ginger bushes, those masses of white and yellow which bordered the path.

Prudently, Linda chose that they should pick their flowers at the back of the Palacio. She took nail scissors from her pocket, told Jacinto he could cut the blossoms he like best, and perhaps it was inevitable that he should select carnations, those flowers which Portugal has made her own. A dozen white and a dozen pink.

'You hold them, Linda,' he said. 'They are for the nursery?'

She nodded. 'We'll find a few sprays of climbing feather to go with them.'

'Wait,' he said shyly. 'Now I find for you a rose.'

'No, Jacinto . . .'

But he had begun to run round the Palacio. She didn't mind, because it was too early to be dangerous, but she did run after him. He took a path down towards the rose beds, but half way along it she laughingly caught him up and flung an arm about him, taking the scissors from his fingers. For a minute or two he forgot he was Jacinto de Filano and fought her, and the two of them tumbled and rolled in the grass. He lay there and gave a sigh of rapture.

'Look at the lovely blue of the sky. We should do this every morning, Linda. It is fun.'

'You've a damp shoulder—I shall get the sack.' She scooped him up and planted him on his feet, felt a faint impact of warning and looked up towards the balconies. She was on her knees with one arm about the boy, the carnations in profusion around her, cornsilk hair tousled and blowing. Luis leaned on his balcony wall, watching them. He wore slacks and a white silk shirt, looked as if he had been up for hours.

She straightened quickly, bade Jacinto help her collect the flowers, and when she had them in her arm she took his hand.

'Good morning,' Luis said clearly. 'I wish you a happy birthday, Jacinto. You both have wetness about the ankles. Go and dress.'

'I wanted to cut a rose for Linda,' Jacinto called in his treble tones.

'You may do so later,' his father answered abruptly. 'Hurry to your rooms!'

As they ran up the stairs Linda said, 'We've misbehaved, Jacinto, but it was good, wasn't it? You'll remember this morning, won't you?'

'Oh, yes. I wish we could have stayed out there.'

'Next time we'll dress first.'

'No, it would not be the same.'

Exactly how she felt herself. Drat the Marquez and his conventions!

She popped Jacinto into the bath and while he played with floating toys she quickly got into uniform. When he was towelled she helped him into his clothes, and turned back the collar of the pale blue shirt.

'Like that, or with a tie?' she asked.

'May I please have no tie?' he demanded eagerly.

'We'll start that way,' she said cautiously. 'Come and see your presents in the nursery.'

Her own gift was a book of half a dozen three-dimensional pictures, which she had brought from England for just such an occasion. Jacinto was enthralled by cavalry standing out on the miniature stage, and turreted forts into which he could actually insert his fingers. His other gifts were large and expensive, but he had seen such things before; streamlined model cars, sets of picture cards, a white-sailed yacht, an elegant glider.

He was examining the glider when Luis came in. Linda prepared herself for a rebuke which did not come. Jacinto told his father he was pleased with the toys and dutifully showed him the Portuguese story books which Tia Velira had sent to the nursery for him.

But this is given to me by Linda,' he said with pride. 'You see, Papa—real horses, and in the next picture a ship.'

'Of the British Navy,' Luis commented. 'And these are Grenadier Guards. It seems your Linda wishes to establish an entente cordiale. You are very lucky this morning, Jacinto.' His glance rested on the crystal vase displaying the carnations as he added, 'You are not disappointed with your gifts?'

'But no,' politely. 'I am delighted.'

'Muito bem. Perhaps later, as Miss Grey insists this is a special day, we shall all go for a ride.' He paused. 'No tie, pequeno?'

'The air felt so good,' said Linda quickly, 'that just for today I let Jacinto please himself, but if you object . . .'

His glance was very foreign as he looked at her. 'You are what the English call a trier—no? I will see you both later in the day.'

Well, he hadn't insisted on the tie, but neither had he mentioned the puppy. She recalled a faintly mocking glint in his eye as he had come into the nursery, and decided he might have been taunting her, in his own fashion, for over-reaching herself once more. The tie was probably a concession because he had chosen to ignore the note. He had known that Jacinto would consider fantastic the demand for a puppy. Certainly the little boy seemed to have forgotten it completely.

The call came for Jacinto to go to Tia Velira's room and receive her blessing, and Linda put on the tie and sent him in alone. When he came back to the nursery he discarded the tie himself. Tia Velira had a headache, he said, and would not get up till lunch-time; in the same breath he asked if they might have their mid-morning chocolate downstairs.

Linda had found that she did not take to the chocolate-drinking habit. She had asked for, and been granted, an electric kettle, and whenever she did not fancy coffee or chocolate she made tea for herself in the nursery. Almost automatically some blue and white china cups and plates with a matching teapot had appeared on the top shelf of the nursery cupboard, and three folded teacloths appeared in the linen cupboard in the bathroom.

This morning, however, she did as Jacinto wished, and took him down to the side terrace for chocolate. He ate his usual fancy biscuit and for a treat broke one for the birds. They were deciding which toys to take on their walk when the white car drove round below the terrace and Luis, seeing them, put on the brake.

He got out and came up the side steps. 'I am free till lunch-time. Where shall we go—to find a mountain?'

'To find a river,' said Jacinto promptly.

Luis lifted a thick dark brow. 'The little tongue is loose this morning. Very well, we shall find a river. The poor Tia is not able to go with us.'

As usual, Jacinto's hand took hold of Linda's, and he went down the steps with her and slipped into the front seat.

'You, too, Miss Grey,' said Luis. 'There is plenty of room. You are comfortable?'

'Very. I'll take Jacinto on my knee so that he can see everything. There, that's splendid. I don't know your countryside, darling, so you must explain things to me as we go along.'

'I presume,' said Luis, as they moved down the drive, 'that you were then addressing the child.'

She smiled. 'I'm sure you were never in doubt.'

'About that, no. There are things about you which puzzle me and I could still find it easy to be angry with you—but for this morning we have a truce. You have not travelled this road away from Merida?'

'No. Doesn't it go right down through the Valle das Flores?'

'To the river,' he added, 'and along its bank to the source. Some time you must see where the river begins. In Merida we have a feast in which the river is much used, and it is said that on the day there is a strange power in the water at the source where it bubbles through the rocks. One drinks if one is unhappy and the problem is solved.'

'How convenient. Do you know anyone who's proved it?'

'No,' he said with a smile, 'but I know of couples who have gone there to prove it and come away reconciled. You will say they could have kissed and made up anywhere, but to them that is not true. They would have it that there is a special grace in the waters of the Gruta de Santa Maria.'

'There's a goat-boy,' murmured Jacinto.

'And the goats,' she said. 'I hope he'll keep them away from the flowers.'

'Linda likes flowers,' Jacinto told his father.

'So I have observed,' returned Luis. 'Did you cut the rose?'

'I forgot. Tia Velira says it is wicked to forget such things.'

'Not wicked,' said Linda. 'You won't forget next time.'

Jacinto turned once more to the Marquez. 'Linda always forgives,' he informed him with a relieved sigh. 'I am never afraid that she will be cross.'

'In the small courtesies,' said his father sternly, 'it can never be right to forget. Linda forgives because you are young, but she would naturally be happy if you did not forget.'

'We seem to be descending quite quickly,' put in Linda tactfully. 'The vineyards look rich, but I don't see any grapes.'

'They are still small and green,' said Luis, slowing down. 'Look carefully along the lanes under the pergolas and you will see that the vines are laden. Those which you eat at table have been forced. I think you will like the harvest and the wine-making. It is a busy time in the valley, with much noise and dancing, and we have a special evening of vinho verde at the Palacio.'

'What is vinho verde—green wine?'

'Immature wine, fresh from new casks. One drinks only a little because it has an extraordinary potency. We ship no wine of any kind before it is two years old. As with the cork from the forests, we sell only the best.' He waved a hand. 'You now see the river—a gentle one. The pink flowers near the bank are margaritas and the mauve ones higher up are wild orchids. We shall stop here under the oak tree and walk down.'

It was just as he closed the car doors after them that a priest roared by on a well-worn motor-scooter. Luis raised a hand, the priest did the same, gaily. It was the first time Linda had seen a padre on a scooter; not the last, though.

She looked round at the sweep of the valley. They were on one side of a long, shallow bowl which had the river coursing lazily among its greenery. Far away on the opposite side a tiny white cottage nestled here and there among trees, but in this expanse there seemed to be no cultivation. Only myriads and myriads of flowers in all the shades from pastel pink, through the blues to a deep violet.

As they neared the river she heard its placid gurgling over the stones, and a moment later she saw the crystal clear waters, the sandy bed between the boulders. The little collars of foam gave off a glaring whiteness in the midday heat, and Luis drew them into the shade of an ancient olive.

'There are much more interesting sights than this in Merida,' he said, 'but it is what Jacinto has asked for, and today he has his way. You find it too warm, Miss Grey?'

'No, it's marvellous.'

'Oh, yes, I remember. You think you must have the warm-blooded ancestors! I wonder what they were, those ancestors!'

'Just countryfolk,' she said. 'Do you think Jacinto might paddle?'

'Like a camponinho? I think not!'

'I can never resist the water on hot days. We're absolutely alone. Do let him just put his toes in!'

'No. We will walk under the trees, and then drive a little more. Come Jacinto.'

But the type of outing was so unusual for Jacinto that he was not too sure what was expected of him. Instinctively he began to behave as any other boy of his age might have behaved in like circumstances. He ran a short way ahead, became absorbed in something he could see on the ground, and then wandered a few yards up the bank and found a twig with which to prod at the earth between the grasses and flowers.

The footpath was cobbly and narrow, and automatically Luis put a hand to Linda's elbow. And there, as she walked slowly beside the warm river in dappled sunshine with that magnetic hand close to her side, a strange thing seemed to happen within Linda. She couldn't name it because it was too complex, and she had the sudden fatal conviction that nothing would ever be simple again. Almost blindly she looked up the bank at the boy, then her arm contracted in Luis' grasp. These two, she thought faintly. These two . . .

Luis was saying, 'So I am afraid it is something you must not do again. It did not vex me, you understand? The pleasure of running out in the early morning is peculiar to young people; the old, however, are apt to be shocked by such things. Also, our household is not so constituted that a young woman living there may be uninhibited.'

'It was very early,' she managed. 'I didn't think for a moment that we'd be seen.'

He was smiling. 'You looked sweet and small. Tumbling in the grass you might have been brother and sister. It is the first time I have seen Jacinto play so happily.'

She might have said, 'He'd tumble just as happily with a puppy,' but it didn't come to her mind. Just then it was difficult to think of anything very clearly. There was the hand which kept a companionable hold on her elbow, his shoulder above her own, the proud, half-smiling features turned down towards her; and there was a most uncanny sensation at the back of her throat.

'I won't let it happen again,' she assured him in low tones.

She felt a change in the way he was looking at her, but did not raise her head.

'I have offended you,' he said quietly.

'Not at all. I'm the one who offended.'

'That is not true. In a way, it made me anxious to see you out in the garden like that, but it was purely for your sake. One or two servants were about, and the maids come on duty at seven.'

'I won't let it happen again,' she repeated.

He gestured impatiently. 'You are letting it become import-ant. Why do you not laugh it off, as you treat everything else?'

'Aren't you serious, then?'

'Of course I am serious!'

'In that case, why should I laugh it off?'

'Because,' he said deliberately, 'I notice that you are serious even when you shrug off a situation with a smile. The fact that you are not smiling now indicates something much more grave. I will not have you regard this in such a way. It is nothing. If it means so much to you, you may do it again tomorrow!'

She did smile then, faintly. 'Oh, no, not again. I won't try my luck too far. If Doña Velira . . .'

'I have already told Doña Velira that your behaviour is my concern. She has authority only over your guidance of the child. Remember that!'

'Very well, senhor. But I don't wish to disturb *you* in any way, either.'

'That is very kind of you, Miss Grey,' he said with sarcasm, and their former light companionableness was restored.

But Linda couldn't recover inwardly with such speed. She had never been so conscious of anyone, never known herself so hypersensitive even to an inflection. Perhaps it was fortun-ate that the little boy came running to her with a scratched finger. Almost gratefully she dropped to his side and took a clean handkerchief from her pocket.

It was a small scratch but it bled. She squeezed the flesh and dabbed it clean, refolded the handkerchief so that he could have it bound in a deliciously bulky bandage round the finger, and to finish off the small incident she placed a tiny kiss on the tip of his nose.

'You are an artist,' Luis commented. 'Already you are able to do as you will with the child. I wonder if you are as successful with adult relationships?'

'Adults get out of hand,' she replied in her normal manner.

'You mean Rico?' he said, as they turned back along the bank. 'I would say he is easy for a woman to manage. He is aware of two blue eyes and in no time at all he is sure he is in love.'

'That's because something always has to be happening to him or life is too dull.' She paused. 'You don't believe in him as an airman, do you?'

'The pilot's licence he showed me was genuine.'

'Has he ever gone so far in any other direction?'

His glance at her was calculating. 'No, but it is still not the career one would choose for him. Can you imagine how I would feel if I financed this scheme of his and through it he lost his life?'

'I hadn't thought about that angle,' she said slowly. 'Even though you refused to help him you must have turned it over in your mind. I'm glad.'

'For Rico?'

'I suppose so. But I'm also glad that you haven't been cold and distant about it. I was afraid you had.'

'So I am more tolerable?' he asked with humour. Without waiting for her reply, he added, 'You see now that it would be best for him to forget this thing?'

She looked at him fleetingly. 'It's a case of how strongly he feels, isn't it? If he's really keen he'll try to get the money elsewhere. Would you believe in him, then?'

He smiled. 'I can promise you that, but it is not likely to happen, because Rico does not inspire confidence. Let us go up to the car.'

They had lingered rather longer near the river than he had intended, and as it was getting near one o'clock he turned the car towards the Palacio. Jacinto lay back sleepily against Linda and said he was hungry.

'It may take him a few days to get used to the new lunch hour,' she said, 'but he did get up early this morning, and it's been more exciting than usual.'

'And your morning?' Luis queried carelessly. 'Has that been unusual?'

'Most unusual,' she returned, almost inaudibly.

'Have you never before walked among flowers with a man?'

She hesitated, made her voice light. 'Not those flowers, senhor.'

'It is strange, I think,' said Luis in the same casual tones, 'that we two who disapprove of each other should nevertheless contrive a certain friendliness. You feel you could be happy with us for years, Miss Grey?'

'Sometimes.'

'But at other times you become very conscious of the differences in race and temperament, and vexed by what it pleases you to call the narrowness of our way of life. Tell me,' he sounded very suave, 'which is it that you find most irksome—the small restrictions which are necessarily placed upon your own movements, or the fact that we do not quite agree upon what is good for the young?'

'I'm here to work, senhor. It naturally comes first.'

'I guessed you would say that, but I also do not forget that recently you called me a tyrant—and it was not in connection with your work!'

She smiled. 'As the head of the household you're not a tyrant, senhor; you're merely an autocrat, and at Rawson Hall they didn't teach us how to deal with autocrats.'

'No?' with mockery. 'Yet you do very well, I think.'

'I'm learning by experience, and I slip up now and then. But I go on trying.'

'I am aware of exactly what you want and how far I can let you go.'

'Well, nothing worthwhile can be done in a hurry,' she returned philosophically.

'Thank you,' he said smoothly, and turned the car in between the portals of the Palacio Filano.

He drew up at the foot of the steps, came round to lift out the child and give Linda his hand. For a moment he looked at another car which stood just in front of his own dashing model. This other was a black two-seater of doubtful year, and it had the appearance of a brave, poor relation. Luis shrugged, walked along the terrace and opened the first door into the sala. He stood aside while Linda went in with Jacinto, entered the room and stood still, his teeth very white in a welcoming smile.

'Deus! It is Nolette herself. And you have become even more beautiful! We have waited so long for this, Nolette!'

He had both the woman's hands in his, touched his lips to one wrist and then to the other, and still holding the hands he leaned back slightly to appraise her with delight and warmth.

'Ah, Luis!' come the husky riposte. 'Ever the gallant. I will match you. I have longed for this moment ever since the day I left Merida, six years ago!'

'It has been a lifetime! But the car . . .' He had released her hands and was greeting Doña Velira.

'The car is Mr Cullum's,' said Nolette del Carros. 'He was good enough to drive me here.'

Michael Cullum had been standing in the shadow between two windows, but he came forward now and shook Luis' hand. Luis turned towards Linda and the child.

'Today is our little one's birthday and we have taken him for a ride to the river. May I present his nurse, Miss Grey?'

'Hullo, Linda,' said Mike.

'So?' said Luis, pausing critically. 'You two have known each other in England?'

'No, we met at Eve's,' Mike answered. 'Last Sunday.'

'And already you have the familiar way with each other,' commented Luis coolly. 'Both you and Nolette will stay to lunch, of course. Miss Grey, we will postpone the new arrangement till tomorrow. The boy is tired, and it would be best to give him his lunch now and let him rest.'

Mike said quickly, 'When shall I see you, Linda?'

But somehow Luis was already at the door and bowing out Linda and the child with the utmost charm. And Linda wasn't sorry to leave them for the privacy of the nursery. She was beginning to feel quite ragged at the edges.

CHAPTER FIVE

FROM that morning when Nolette del Carros arrived, a subtle change came over the Palacio, and because it was propagated by Doña Velira the change quickly lost some of the subtlety but gained in strength. The senhora's personal maid, Lupe, a most discreet woman unless she became excited, found herself spilling small gossip to a corridor maid, and the corridor maid, who was occasionally on duty while Jacinto rested and Linda went for a walk, let slip some enthralling titbits of news.

Linda couldn't help forming a picture and adding details. She recalled the jolt of that first meeting in the sala, the way her senses had quivered into alertness. If she had thought at all before of Nolette del Carros, it was in an idle way; what would such a woman be like, she had wondered—this Portuguese sculptress? The answer had not seemed important.

Then she had seen the woman. Dark hair parted in the middle and drawn back into a chignon, thin straight nose and big dark eyes within heavy fringes, a skin like magnolia blossoms, a defined mouth, a long and lovely neck. Narrow shoulders clad in a gay blouse which buttoned at the wrists, a pencil-slim skirt, tiny black shoes with tall heels.

There is an occasional woman whom all men find desirable. And Linda knew with deadly certainty that Nolette was one of them. She was about twenty-seven, and that rare creature, a Portuguese woman who had been permitted to study and work at the thing she most loved. Within a few hours Linda learned more.

Nolette had been exceptionally fortunate in her father. He himself had loved sculpture, and when he discovered her gift nothing else had mattered. She had studied with him, and when she had come of age he had sent her to Lisbon with a duenna, then to Madrid and Paris. It was whispered among the servants that she had gone away only a few days before the Marquez had married, and Lupe, it seemed, had it from Doña Velira herself that Nolette had returned at Luis' invitation. It was only a matter of time . . .

Linda hardened herself and kept her mind as much as possible on Jacinto. The day after his birthday she took him

73

down to lunch at one-thirty, but Luis was out, and with Doña Velira at the head of the table the meal passed almost in silence.

On Saturday morning she had a note from Michael Cullum: 'So sorry I didn't get a word with you when I called, but I have your boss's permission to take you out this afternoon. Will call for you at two. Bring a bathing suit.'

Linda's heart lifted. She took Jacinto for his walk, had lunch with him downstairs in an otherwise empty dining-room, and saw him into bed for his rest. The maid took over, and Linda changed into a button-through flowered print and looked out the white swim suit. She wasn't exhilarated, but it would definitely be a relief to get away from the Palacio after the unrest of recent days.

She went downstairs at exactly two, heard laughter from the sala and decided on the front door. She stepped into the mosaic porch just as Mike's car slowed outside, and a swift smile came to her lips. They met at the foot of the steps.

'Such punctuality means one of two things,' he commented. 'You're either glad to see me or glad to get out. In this case I'll flatter myself.'

'You may, but it's both, really.' She slipped into the seat of the open car. 'I love silly old buses like this. Where on earth did you get it?'

'Have respect, please.' He let in the clutch gently, as if hum-ouring the thing. 'I came away from England by plane, and I was too fed up to think of shipping my own car. Eve and John can't often spare theirs, so I've been trying all week to hire one in Portão. This delicious thing has been lying up for about five years in someone's garage. I persuaded the owner to part with it, and I'll get someone to buy it from me at a bargain price when I return to England. Rico says he might like her. She goes, doesn't she?'

Indeed, the little vehicle spurted away from the Palacio like a startled buck, but out on the road it settled down, and Linda thought how good it was to feel the wind in her hair, and to know that this man at her side had no Latin complica-tions to his nature. There was nothing in the least oppressive about Mike Cullum.

They exchanged a few platitudes, and Linda repeated to herself, with a sort of despairing defiance, that she much pre-ferred men who left one in no doubt as to what they meant. She liked Mike's sandy colouring, too. It was safe and neutral.

74

'So you've seen Rico,' she said. 'Had any binges?'

'Nothing big. The chap seems to be stymied.'

'Has he told you anything about himself?'

Mike nodded. 'I've heard it all, and been sworn to secrecy. He doesn't know what to do.'

'Well, I'm out of it, thank heaven. But if you like you can tell him that Luis might be more inclined to help if he showed more initiative. Luis just doesn't believe Rico is sincere and a stayer. He has to have proof.'

'I've worked too hard myself to have much sympathy for the type who expect planes to fall into their laps.' He waved a hand towards the lavender-tinted peaks, the cork forests climbing the hillsides. 'Soft, sunlit mountains. That's the best of the south. Where would you rather bathe—river or lake?'

'So there's a choice! Lake, please.'

'Thought so—that's where we're going. There's a goat-boy's hut where you can change, and fine clear water.'

'You remember it from two years ago?'

'Partly, but I went along and checked up yesterday.' He added pleasantly, 'I've some good news for you. I've shifted all my belongings to Eve's house in Merida. I'll be around whenever you have time to spare.'

'You're not going back to Portão?'

'Not to live. I like Merida—and the people here. Can you get out in the evenings?'

'I may get permission, seeing that you're English. But there's nowhere to go.'

'Leave that to me.'

She smiled. 'You've lost some of the droop. Feeling better?'

'Oh, sure. My trouble when I first arrived was that I'd stopped working and there was nothing to take its place. But quite suddenly I've plenty to think about. This car is an occupation in itself. Can you drive?'

'No, but I know all the moves. Are you going to offer to teach me?'

'Why not? In this world you can never know too much. Look, there's the lake.'

It was a small lake with groups of lemons and olives on its further bank and a belt of reeds where wild ducks nested. A white road curved round its edge and climbed between tangles of nut and berry trees to a white-walled convent which clung to the hillside. The whole scene was somnolent under the hot blue sky, and even the convent chimes were tiny muted sounds without echo.

Mike found the goatherd's hut and pulled in behind it. 'Let's have our swim right away,' he said, 'and then we'll be able to rest in comfort. Shall I use the hut first?'

'Yes, please.'

'Right. I'll give you a shout when I'm through.'

Ten minutes later they were floating and desultorily swimming in the blue waters of the lake. A few birds drifted overhead, a warm breeze stirred the scent of lemon flowers and an occasional butterfly found itself above the water and struggled back to the blossoms on the bank. It being the hour of siesta there was no one about, and they were able to sunbathe for a while before dressing.

Mike drove up the white road, past the convent and over the hill into a village of red and white houses and earth yards where chickens scratched and dogs lazily twitched away flies. A donkey whose ears poked through holes in a sun-hat champed slowly at a ragged bundle of hay which had been lodged between himself and the shafts of his cart, and another donkey lay right in the centre of the road licking a new foal.

'The ubiquitous donkey,' said Mike. 'It's as easy as that.' They turned a corner and he pointed over a low, crenellated wall at a manorial quinta which had cupolas and fretted ironwork, balustraded steps and dozens of stone urns festooned with flowers. 'Simplicity and magnificence next door to each other. Don't you sometimes feel the Palacio is overpowering?'

'Very often. The other day the servants were cleaning those ceiling paintings and carvings and the chandeliers in the small sala, and I looked round and reflected that it was only one room out of thirty or forty. Anyone growing up there is likely to be a bit ... outlandish. That's why I feel I must fight for Jacinto. It's not an ideal place for a child to live.'

He grinned. 'Have you told Luis that?'

'Not yet, but the day may come! Where are we going, Mike?'

'This is a straggling village with a café at the end. I'm afraid we shan't get tea.'

'Just something liquid and a cigarette,' she said with a luxurious sigh.

They found seats under a huge acacia, Mike roused the café owner and they were given wine and some small hard tasty pellets which neither could analyse. Linda leaned on the table and looked down the deserted dusty street at a splendid stone column surmounted by a cross.

'I suppose these churches and palaces mean more to a man like you than to anyone else,' she said. 'You know rococo and baroque as soon as you see them, and you can probably pick out the dates of new additions to a building. Are you on a sort of busman's holiday?'

He shook his head. 'I did it all last time I came here. I shan't be able to resist looking over a few churches but I haven't any plans. By the way, have you spoken to Nolette del Carros?'

A shadow came over the sun. 'I'm not likely to have anything to do with her,' Linda said. 'Is she clever?'

'She's brilliant, but not original.' Mike rested an elbow on the table and his chin on his hand, and for him, he looked eager. 'I'd heard of her—it must be more than a year ago. There was an exhibition in London and she entered a model— a replica of a famous monastery near Lisbon. It was the most remarkable piece of copying I've ever seen, and I looked around for some information about her. So naturally I more or less knew her career before we met. Actually her old father lives down the avenida from Eve's house and he asked me to call in there as soon as Nolette arrived. I did so at about ten o'clock on Thursday morning, and it was all so interesting that I hung on too long. Their own car was supposed to be taking her to the Palacio, but I was keen to see you again, so I brought her along. You know, for a Portuguese she's a most outstanding woman.'

'Does she work at all—I mean, to earn money?'

'The del Carros family seem to be well off, but she does get commissions.' He gave a brief deprecating laugh. 'She says she's giving it up because it's time people realised she's a woman.'

'She looks to me to be all woman.'

'Yes, but she's different from other Portuguese. She's not one of your beautiful silent wenches. She's been around and can talk, she's accomplished a good deal, and yet she still has a tremendous respect for the male.'

Linda twisted her empty glass. 'Do you think she came home to see Luis?'

'Could be, couldn't it? When her father and I were alone for a few minutes he told me she's had two or three proposals and

77

not considered any of them.'

'But if Luis is the attraction why hasn't she come before? Would she have waited for an invitation from him?'

Mike's eagerness had dimmed and he had a little of the tired, moody look. 'Heaven knows. Maybe she's occasionally taken soundings and this time they were favourable. I wouldn't know how their minds work.'

But Linda couldn't yet leave it alone. 'It's rumoured at the Palacio that Luis is at the back of her visit, and they did meet enthusiastically, didn't they?'

Mike nodded, said with a frankness that he could not know was brutal, 'She's just Luis' dish, really—intelligent, of good Portuguese family, fine-looking and sophisticated enough for the position she'd have to take in Merida. Eve says his first marriage was doomed before it began but he was too chivalrous to back out of it. She thinks Nolette had fallen for him and went away for that reason.' He lifted his shoulders. 'It couldn't happen anywhere else but here!'

'These love affairs,' said Linda, 'become tiring. I don't mean yours, Mike. You were darned unfortunate.'

He refilled his glass from the wine carafe. 'A smashed romance is supposed to put one off women, isn't it? But I don't feel that way. I suppose I'm afraid I'm lacking in some direction and am anxious to prove that I'm not. You know, Linda, I ought to have fallen for someone like you.'

'You'll have your chance. There are plenty more like me in England.'

He gave her a jaded look. 'You're wrong. However, let it pass. But if you ever feel like taking a guy on the rebound, I'm all yours.'

'Thanks,' she said in mock earnest. 'Getting a bit morbid, aren't we?'

He took his drink in one go. 'Come on, I'll give you that driving lesson. Nothing like a woman behind the wheel to keep one's feet on the ground!'

She laughed. 'That sounds like one of Rico's proverbs. You'd better explain the car's personality before we start moving!'

During the next couple of hours they forgot each other and the Palacio. In experienced hands Mike's was a wayward vehicle and with Linda at the wheel it showed even more temperament. When at last they landed back in Merida both were grubby and pleasantly spent. In the early darkness a few bright lights shone from the houses on the avenida, but the Bayes' villa was in total darkness.

'Apparently they didn't make it,' Mike remarked. 'There was some sort of afternoon function in Portão, and Eve said if it ended too late they wouldn't turn up before tomorrow morning. Come in for a wash and a bite, anyway.'

'Only a wash. I have to get back to the Palacio.'

Mike braked on the dark drive. 'I understood you were free for the whole day.'

'So I am, but as I've been there each Saturday to see Jacinto to bed they'll expect me.'

'But you don't really have to go?'

'Well, no, but I think I'd better.'

'If you're afraid Luis will be waiting with a carpet slipper, you needn't be. He was due at the del Carros mansion at six—a sort of cocktail party to welcome Nolette, and then they're going to a special show at the Estrella in Portão.'

Something went a little cold within Linda. She reflected that if she did go straight to the Palacio, a long lethal evening would stretch in front of her. The servant in charge of Jacinto knew that Miss Grey was entitled to be free from noon onwards, and she would see that he had his supper and went to bed at the correct time.

'What is the Estrella?' she asked.

'A sort of night club on discreet lines. You have dinner at about ten o'clock, then there's a floor show and dancing till about two in the morning. It's one of those outlandishly expensive places.'

'I never thought of Luis in . . . that kind of setting.'

'He doesn't go often, but this is a special occasion. Why shouldn't he step out with his girl friend, anyway? I'll bet they look quite something when they're together.'

'Do you think the two of them will go to Portão alone?'

'That was the arrangement, I believe; they made it on Thursday, at lunch-time. Luis is above reproach, of course, and Nolette doesn't have to measure up to local standards.'

A brief silence. Then Linda said: 'All right, I'll have that wash and a snack, if you can find one. I almost wish we could go dancing ourselves, don't you?'

'That's the girl,' said Mike. 'Come on in. There are no servants about, so we'll have to eat in the kitchen. I'm a genius with ham and eggs!'

But the liveliness of each of them that evening was forced.

They didn't cook, after all, but ate a few leftovers and made tea. Mike found a couple of ancient dance records and rolled back the rugs, but dancing was heavy going, and there was a moment when Linda's nerves became painfully taut. It was when Mike stopped his shuffling and tightened his arm about her, dropping his cheek against hers. She felt his unhappiness and need and it made her sick with a nameless longing.

'I'd rather you didn't,' she whispered.

He kept his mouth close to her hair. 'Falling in love doesn't work out,' he said unevenly. 'Why don't we decide we're made for each other, get married and forget everyone else? With two sane people it should be possible.' But when she made no answer, he added below his breath, 'For some reason I made the mistake of thinking that you feel as left-behind as I do. Forgive me?'

'That's all right, Mike. We've been alone together for too many hours.' She released herself. 'Will you take me to the Palacio?'

'Let me get some coffee first,' he begged. 'I meant us to finish up tonight on a high note, so that you'd want to see me again.'

'Of course I do, but bathing and the strain of trying to drive that car of yours have made me sleepy. Still, I wouldn't mind a cup of coffee.'

Mike's relief took the form of a burst of activity, and he made Linda sit down at the kitchen table till the coffee was ready. He talked a lot while they drank, told her about his student days and a partnership he was hoping for, and when the cups were empty he put them on the draining board. Linda picked up the jug of milk and carried it towards the huge antiquated refrigerator which stood in a recess that once had held a coal stove. Her nerves must still have been jumpy, because when Mike came to manipulate the great steel handle she hurriedly dragged at it herself to avoid his closeness. Quite what happened to her hand she could never afterwards re-collect in detail. The heavy door opened and she slipped the jug on to the top shelf; then somehow in her haste the left hand was caught between the steel door and the frame before it was swiftly wrenched free.

She must have exclaimed, because Mike said quickly, 'Hurt yourself?'

'Not much. I didn't realise the fridge door was so heavy.'

'It's one of the old has-beens, but it does its job and a new one the same size would cost the earth. Sure your hand is all right?'

She nodded. 'I really must go, Mike.'

Actually, the hand was numb for almost ten minutes, and they weren't far from the Palacio when the pain started somewhere near the knuckle of her middle finger. Pain, heat and throbbing. Bruised tissues, she thought; it would be stiff tomorrow.

She thanked Mike and said goodnight, went straight into the quietude of the hall and up to her room. Jacinto was sleeping, the maid murmured something and went away. Linda looked at the swollen purpling mass in the middle of her left hand, back and front, and decided to paint the whole area with iodine. She would simply have to be patient till it healed. She ought to be grateful for the pain; it certainly kept her mind occupied.

Linda was again free from noon onwards the following day, but she did not go out. Because there were several guests for lunch, Jacinto ate upstairs, but at four o'clock, while he was dressing after his rest, a servant came up with a message. Miss Grey was asked to come down to tea with the child. Linda looked at her hand, decided it would be impossible to keep it in her pocket the whole time, and sent Jacinto down with the servant.

'Please tell the senhor that I'm off-duty this afternoon. Quietly, so that no one else can hear.'

'The Senor Marquez knows that,' the man returned. 'But he is aware that you are here in your room.'

'Well, tell him I'm very tired,' she said, and repeated, 'Tell him quietly.'

The servant was scandalised. Even Doña Velira had to be laid out in bed before she would refuse a request from the Marquez. However, the English miss was palpably in no mood to give in, and he would have to obey.

Linda sat for a while with a book in her balcony, but she did not read much. She looked down over the lawns, at the different shades of green in the more distant trees, at the folds of the hills beyond, which an amazing fertility clothed with vines and peach trees, with wheat and maize, olive trees and flower gardens.

Presently she went into the nursery to make some tea, noticed that someone had replaced the carnations with red and white camellias. As she stood for a moment looking at the flowers she knew with certainty that they had been placed there at Luis' command. She remembered Jacinto telling his father that she loved flowers, and Luis' appraisal of the bouquet she had placed in the vase. She wished to heaven he'd forget the courtesies once in a while!

After a cup of tea she felt better, though it did occur to her that it would have been wonderful to share it with someone. In England there had been nothing she enjoyed more than having a couple of friends in for tea on Sunday; teatime had always stretched out into the evening, and she had invariably wailed at the swift flight of time. Heavens, she mustn't start regretting this; it must be the throbbing of the injured hand that made her feel low.

At about five-thirty Jacinto came back. In reply to her inquiry he told Linda politely that he had enjoyed himself; there had been only Papa and Tia Velira, and after a little while Papa had gone away and Lupe had come to call Tia. No, he hadn't played, only sat down at the table and had lemonade with cake.

'We'll go down to the garden,' Linda said. 'You deserve a good run after sitting still for so long.'

She was keyed up to feel more angry than usual at the lack of childish excitement in his life. And when they were safely out of sight of the house she ran with him, let him beat her, and pretended she was lost, so that as the first shadows of dusk fell Jacinto had to find the way back for them both. He did it triumphantly, but as they entered the Palacio he went quiet once more. She wondered, as they went up the staircase, whether these glorious rooms and corridors had ever echoed with the shrill joy of children.

Jacinto had his supper and went downstairs with a maid to say goodnight. After he had got into bed he was not very sleepy, so Linda opened the big book of Portuguese nursery tales and sat down to read one of them to him. Usually he smiled at her accent, but tonight he merely became bored. Halfway through the story she closed the book.

'I'll tell you an English story in Portuguese,' she said. 'It's about a little boy who loved pigs.'

He found that more amusing, because Linda brazenly used

82

an English word whenever she was stuck for the Portuguese, which was often, and he had to correct her. It had run on for quite five minutes when she realised that someone had come into the room and was listening. She looked round, saw the carefully tailored figure of Nolette del Carros with Luis just behind her, and stopped speaking.

'Please go on,' said Nolette, in the attractive husky tones. 'What did this small Jack do when all his pigs but the pretty one had been eaten by the fox?'

Linda stood up. 'I really don't know. I was improvising.'

'But you would have given it a happy ending, no?' said Luis.

'Naturally, senhor.' Linda's left hand slipped into her pocket and she stepped back, as though to leave them.

But Nolette held up a long, spatulate-fingered hand. 'Do not go. I have arrived early for dinner here, and asked Luis if I might come up and properly make the acquaintance of the small Jacinto.' She came to the bed and held out both hands to take the child's, changed to Portuguese. 'How are you, my little one? I am very happy to know you. I am Nolette.'

'Bom dias, senhora,' he returned automatically.

Nolette sat in Linda's chair, leaned forward and spoke to him softly and carefully. Linda stood back in the shadows and watched. She saw the child answer unemotionally, smile faintly, and listen to the low, thrilling voice. She saw Luis standing there at the foot of the carved bed, seemingly absorbed in the reaction these two had upon one another. She wondered if he really loved the child, or whether that rigid sense of duty and the knowledge that the boy was his were what guided his decision about Jacinto's upbringing. It appeared obvious that he wanted these two to like each other.

Nolette leaned forward and kissed Jacinto's forehead, then stood up. Luis smiled and said to the child, 'Will you sleep without knowing the end of your Linda's story? I confess I am somewhat curious myself.'

'I'll tell him as I tuck him in,' said Linda.

Nolette put in charmingly, 'But what happens to this pretty pig who is left so lonely in the sty?'

Linda met Luis' glance briefly, but had time to notice a hard mockery in the bright dark eyes. She said deliberately, 'Well, it was such a baby pig that it couldn't be left alone, and the little boy was lonely too. So his father made a box for the

83

piglet and filled it with straw. In the kitchen the pig was safe from the fox and the little boy gained a delightful companion.'

'Until the pig grew very large and fat,' said Luis, 'when he had to be put out.'

'I suppose so,' Linda nodded, tingling from the challenge in the slight taunt. 'After that, his father bought him a dog, which was both a good companion to the boy and the pig, because he kept away the fox. So everything ended splendidly.'

Almost desperately, she wished then that Jacinto were wide enough awake to take up the implication. Just a very small indication that he remembered asking his father for a puppy and had been disappointed would have been enough. But the dark head was lying back on the pillow and he was obviously waiting for them to go; not for anything would he have been so impolite as to close his eyes while his father and the strange senhora were in the room. The child's uncaring sleepiness was as good a reply as Luis could wish to make himself.

He signed courteously to the other woman that they must leave. Nolette murmured something to Linda and passed in front of him; Luis smiled a small set smile at Linda before following Nolette and closing the door after them.

As Linda tucked in the bedclothes and kissed Jacinto's cheek, she felt herself trembling slightly. An elusive French perfume hovered in the air over the bed, and she pegged the window wider and took in a breath from outdoors. Then she followed the ritual, locking the balcony door, adjusting the curtains, opening her own bedroom door just a foot, switching off the light.

She opened the outer door, said her usual, 'Goodnight, darling, sleep tight,' and closed it after her.

Opposite, the nursery door was wide open. Luis and Nolette were in there, and as he saw Linda he half-bowed and beckoned. She entered the room, to hear Nolette saying with appealing eagerness:

'He has such a good head, Luis! I've never felt so drawn to modelling anyone in my life. You must let me do it, please!'

'We will ask Miss Grey,' he said tolerantly. Then, with that faint air of sarcasm, 'Miss Grey, would you say that Jacinto at the age of four should be perpetuated in bronze?'

Linda was feeling a little cold. 'Certainly, if you wish it yourself.'

'You think he has a good head?'

84

Nolette said gently, 'I hardly think Miss Grey is qualified to judge. Do you know anything about such things, Miss Grey?'

'Nothing at all, I'm afraid.'

'You see?' She shrugged and turned to Luis. 'Is not my opinion enough?'

'It is more than enough,' he said smilingly, 'but Miss Grey already thinks we make the little one sit still for too long.'

'But that is absurd,' remarked Nolette. 'A child must be taught restraint and self-control. I fear,' again the ravishing smile upon those beautifully defined lips, 'that Miss Grey is too young for our type of family. That story of hers just now was very babyish.'

'The baby years end at five, senhora,' said Linda. 'A child has grown out of such stories when he has ceased to enjoy them. It's a great pity to make him grow up too soon.'

Nolette's dark glance slid over her negligently. 'If the Marquez will consent, you may bring Jacinto to my studio, and tell him as many of these tales as you wish, while he sits. Agreed, Luis?'

'Perhaps. As you and Miss Grey have had such different beginnings you may find much of mutual interest. After all, the character which completely opposes one's own has endless possibilities.'

'But no doubt there would not be many grounds for agreement,' Nolette laughed. 'Imagine for yourself, Luis, the bewildering experience of trying to dovetail the English customs with our own. Our two races can be friends but we can never be kin.'

'I think you're right,' Linda said evenly. 'You must let me know when you need Jacinto to be brought to your studio.'

'Let us start soon—on Tuesday. My studio is in my father's house, and perhaps a good time will be from noon till one o'clock.'

'I believe,' said Luis, 'that Miss Grey and Jacinto take their walk at that time.'

'We can walk earlier,' Linda said. 'He won't mind the inaction if he's a bit tired.'

'Thank you, Miss Grey,' said Nolette graciously. 'Tuesday at twelve.'

She began to move out into the corridor, but stopped when Luis said suavely:

'You might care to dine with us this evening, Miss Grey. We have only Nolette and her father, and I feel you would like to meet Senhor del Carros. He has studied many of your old English buildings.'

Linda smiled mechanically, ignoring the ache in her throat. 'Thank you, senhor, but I'm still off duty and have a few jobs to do.'

A stony brilliance came into the dark eyes. 'Is that how you would regard dining with us—as a duty?'

'Of course not. I thought you were simply being kind, and I want you to know it isn't necessary. I really am rather tired.'

'You are afraid I did not believe your excuse this afternoon?'

'It's a perfectly true one. I had a long day out yesterday, and did some things I'm not accustomed to.'

'With Cullum? What things?'

'We had a swim, and then I tried to drive that car of his. It was exhausting.'

Unsmiling, he asked, 'At what time did he bring you home?'

'Not very late. Before ten.'

Nolette tapped an impatient shoe.

Luis said coldly, 'Very well, Miss Grey, you are tired. I see now that you are paler than usual. Have your meal early and go to bed. I will speak to you tomorrow.'

'Yes, senhor.'

'Goodnight, Miss Grey,' murmured Nolette.

'Goodnight, senhora.'

'Goodnight, my child,' said Luis austerely.

'Goodnight, senhor.'

For some moments after they had gone Linda stood irresolutely in the middle of the nursery. Then she opened all the windows and lit a cigarette; her nerves settled.

Mike was right about them; they suited each other. In time she would accept it herself. Meanwhile Jacinto was her problem. While she remained at Merida she would go on doing her utmost to bring fun into his life.

While she remained at Merida. . . . The words seemed to have a ghostly echo, like a warning.

CHAPTER SIX

WHEN the day began it seemed that Monday might be completely uneventful. Linda had a short session with Doña Velira, and received from her a set of children's school books and instructions to teach Jacinto the pages marked during the course of the week; next Monday, she was told, a new set of pages would be selected, and so on.

She read through the examples of baby arithmetic, the pages of pothooks and the short simple chapter of Portuguese history, and decided to impart the information as far as possible by means of games. It was ridiculous for a four-year-old to be plunged into such books, but there seemed to be some sort of deadlock between herself and the de Filanos. For the present she had to obey.

To Linda, the worst aspect of it all was Jacinto's unquestioning acceptance of whatever might be ordained by Tia Velira. If Linda said, 'Let's walk in a new direction today,' he would ask whether they had permission. Once she had told him lightly that she herself had given them permission, and he had hung back uncertainly. Linda, of course, had inwardly fumed. How could anyone so hemmed in as she was gain the boy's confidence? He showed in many small ways that he was fond of her, but reverence for the family remained stronger, perhaps because it was inherent.

The impulse to defy orders came less often to Linda. After all, what had she gained by stating her own ideas? The matter of the uniform, a slightly happier birthday for Jacinto. But nothing more. One could talk of swings and a sandpit, a see-saw and swimming lessons, less starchy clothing and the necessary playmates, till the cows came home. No one took the slightest notice, and in this the greatest disappointment was Luis. He really had seemed pleased when Jacinto had talked more on his birthday, but somehow, with the advent of Nolette del Carros, everything had slipped back to where it had been before.

She took Jacinto down to lunch, and found Doña Velira already at the foot of the long table. Linda sat at her left and Jacinto was next to Linda. The meal progressed. Linda chose soup, and a salad which could easily be eaten with a fork, and

Jacinto's behaviour was as impeccable as ever. They had reached the fruit and coffee when Luis came in.

He bowed and apologised for being late, poured some wine for Doña Velira and raised an eyebrow at Linda's refusal. He broke a roll, and began to carve from the richly-cured ham which had been placed above his plate.

'You have had troubles, Luis?' asked his aunt.

He smiled at her in the way of a man who never burdens his womenfolk with anything heavier than a compliment. 'Nothing, Tia. My manager was approached by a worker who needs a larger cottage and I saw to it at once. It kept me longer than I thought.'

'But surely these people grumble for nothing!'

'There was no grumbling. Merely the statement of his need. I had forgotten they were now seven in family or I would have arranged it earlier. Has Rico been here?'

'No. The boy worries me. He is staying away for a purpose.'

Luis took salad on to his plate, then looked at Linda. 'You have not seen my cousin, Miss Grey?'

'No, senhor.'

A shrug. 'Do not disturb yourself, Tia. If you need him here we will send a message to his sister.' He took salad dressing, glanced at Linda's fruit plate. 'What will you have, Miss Grey? Apricots, a peach, some grapes?'

'Nothing more, thanks,' she said hastily.

'No?' with his eyebrows lifted sardonically. 'Is not that a bad example to the child? How will he eat fruit if you refuse? Come, try a peach.'

'No, thank you. Would you like some grapes, Jacinto?'

'A peach, please,' the child said quietly.

'Are you sure you don't want grapes?' she asked him a little desperately.

'A peach,' he repeated. 'Will you please peel it for me?'

Linda hoped for a drowning moment that Doña Velira would sternly insist that he try to peel the peach himself. But possibly the senhora thought he might make a spectacle of himself and take too long about it; she said nothing.

Jacinto took the peach on to his plate, Luis got on with his cold meats and salad. Linda bunched her napkin and placed it on the table beyond the fruit plate, dipped her fingers quickly into the silver bowl and took up the peach. She had it peeled

88

and halved, with the stone extracted, when Luis queried, with ominous calm,

'How did you hurt your hand, Miss Grey?'

She rinsed the fingers and used the napkin. 'I caught it in a door, senhor.'

'A room door?'

'No.'

'What kind of door?'

Without hesitation, she said, 'It happened while I was out on Saturday.'

'A car door?'

'No, senhor.'

He didn't press it any further, and at that moment Doña Velira begged to be excused as she was tired, and he got up to escort her to the door. He did not sit down again at once, but stood behind Jacinto's chair.

'You are ready to leave the dining-room, pequeno?'

Obediently, the boy edged off the damask chair. Linda stood up too, and she clasped the small hand which slipped into hers. Luis looked at that other hand.

'When Jacinto has gone to bed I would like to see you again, Miss Grey,' he said. 'Shall we say in a quarter of an hour, on the side terrace?'

'Very well.'

Once more he opened the door. Linda walked out into the cool vastness of the hall, mounted the stairs with Jacinto. She watched the boy take off his outer clothing and shoes, pulled the sheet over him as he lay down.

He said, 'Do you think Papa knows I tried to climb the little tree when we were out this morning?'

She shook her head, smiling at him. 'When you're really good at it we'll show him how clever you are.'

'No, we show Papa with a big tree.'

Linda felt a foolish lump in her throat. It was the first time he had ever confessed to needing his father's pride in him, and she wondered if it had been wise to make him conscious of his feelings. She ruffled his hair and left him in the dimness, but in her own room she stood still near the cheval mirror and surveyed her reflection. Because by lunch-time she had felt the need of a fillip to her feelings, she had replaced her uniform with a white dress dotted with blue cornflowers. It was in a plain rever style with short sleeves, but because of the pattern

89

and the slight stiffness of the material it had a gay look. She had half a mind, now, to change back into uniform, and then it occurred to her that that might place her at a disadvantage with Luis—though she wasn't sure how. At that moment she would have given the earth to be older and more experienced.

However, she did not feel too bad as she made her way downstairs and out on to the terrace. She stood there at the front of the Palacio for a minute, looking at the tiled fountain with its wet stone maiden and at the gold-dusted rain of the waters, and fleetingly she wondered how many women through the ages had come out as she had, and watched those cascading arcs of water as if they held the answer to every problem. She visualised women in elegant black, hair dressed high with ornamental combs, silver lace mantilla fastened with a scarlet rose, or a black mantilla held by a snowy gardenia. Perhaps the frail Amalia had been one of them.

She shivered slightly and walked quickly along the cloistered terrace to its end. Luis was already standing in the wide side terrace, and there were two chairs drawn out on the patterned tiles, close to the low wall, where a flowering plant formed a long cushion and drooped over the stonework in amethyst clusters.

He saw her seated, hitched his trousers and took the other chair, so that both were facing the lawn where the rose beds lay, cream and pink and scarlet in the afternoon sun. Luis opened a thin platinum cigarette case and offered it. He had done this before and she had always declined because she had guessed that was what he expected of a woman. He possibly thought she would shake her head this time, too.

But Linda took one of the long cigarettes, placed the white tip between her lips and bent forward to the flame. He slipped the lighter into his pocket, blew upwards a thin stream of smoke. Curiously, now that he had her at his mercy he seemed disinclined for talk. It was fully a minute before he rested his cigarette on the stone wall, lifted her left hand down from her pocket and let it lie across the palm of his own hand. She felt his fingers stiffen in some sort of reaction to what he saw, the coolness of his palm under hers.

She spoke first, rather quickly. 'It looks worse than it feels—bruises always do.'

'To me,' he said harshly, 'it appears to need medical attention. Why have you done nothing about it?'

'You forget I'm a nurse,' she returned lightly. 'There's no

90

real damage and I've done all that's possible. The swelling has already subsided.''

'You may be right that there is no more one could do for it, but such an injury to a woman's hand is . . .' He broke off, let her withdraw the hand. Abruptly, he said, 'We are now alone. You can tell me how it happened.'

She said frankly, very calmly, 'It was the refrigerator door at Mrs Bayes' house. At the time I thought I'd only numbed it, so Mike doesn't really know about it. There's no need for him to know.'

'You determined that I should not know, either. I noticed the mound of napkin behind which you hoped to hide.'

She smiled resolutely. 'It was the best I could think up on the spur of the moment. Jacinto insisted on the peach and a bruised hand doesn't look well at the dining table.'

'You have a strange set of values,' he commented. 'This poor hand was the reason you would not come to tea or dinner with us yesterday?'

'Partly.'

'For the rest, you did not wish to come?'

She sighed. 'My other excuse was genuine—the tiredness, I mean, and . . . well, I did feel reluctant. I'm sorry if it vexed you.'

'There is something which vexes me more.' He pushed the cigarette he had been smoking down between the mauve flowers, dusted off his fingers. 'Mrs Bayes, I believe, came to Merida for only a few hours yesterday. Michael Cullum took you into the house on Saturday evening knowing there would be no one there.'

'Yes, that's so. But Mike's a steady sort. He wouldn't . . .'

'You are quickly on the defensive, Miss Grey! I am merely stating facts. Now, I must ask you a question. How did you feel about going into that house alone with Cullum? Did you have no fear that it might not be the correct thing to do?'

'I was rather against it, though I couldn't see any real harm in it.'

'I see. You knew it would possibly annoy me very much, but you did it just the same and hoped I would not find out.'

Linda recalled, rather too vividly, her mood last Saturday evening; she looked at Luis' face and found it entirely non-committal. She said evenly, 'You treat me as though I were extraordinarily young, senhor.'

He sounded stern as he answered, 'You are young, very

young. I have never known a woman so young before.'

'But twenty-two isn't juvenile!'

'It is not your age. It is you.' He still spoke without much expression, and there was no sign of a smile. 'Do you ever feel it was wrong to come here—a mistake?'

Linda flicked ash from her skirt, willed the threat of a tremor from her voice. 'I've felt it vaguely, once or twice, but I think one's bound to, in a foreign country. In spite of a few ups and downs, if it was a mistake to come, I'm glad I've made it.'

'Good,' he said quietly. 'That is how I feel myself.'

'You mean I was really a mistaken choice?'

He smiled faintly. 'To be quite honest, I think you were, Miss Grey. What we really wanted was a somewhat younger edition of the former nurse, not someone so youthful and perhaps impetuous as you are. You may not realize that you are also a little highly-strung. However, you are good for the boy and we must be patient with you.'

'Thank you for your forbearance, senhor!'

He gave an alien shrug. 'You see what I mean? Your ways are unsophisticated, Miss Grey. But there is something else.' His manner changed. He leant back in the chair so that she would have to turn her head if she wanted to look at him, and his tones were enigmatic. 'You have some feeling for Michael Cullum?'

'He's very pleasant.'

'It is one of these English friendships—nothing more?'

'Nothing more.'

'Did you stay with him for so many hours on Saturday because you had nothing else to do?'

'In a way—yes.'

'So that I may take it you are . . . lonely?'

Linda turned and pressed out her cigarette in the blue bowl on the table behind them. She took a fleeting glance at him before turning back. With some of his own expressionlessness she answered, 'Not lonely, so much as at a loose end occasionally. I know I can use the car when I wish, but it isn't the same as being able to hike over the countryside whenever I have time and feel like it.'

'Then we must do something about it,' he said. 'And what of other things? Occasionally, when I take a short walk before bed, I have noticed a light in your window. I have listened, but have never heard the radio.'

A queer electric current seemed to pass over Linda's skin.

Luis, listening meticulously for the radio below her window! What sort of a man was this, who seldom missed a detail yet had so little time for his son?

'On the radio everything is in Portuguese,' she said. 'I do sometimes listen to musical programmes. The plays are beyond me.'

A pause. Then: 'I am sounding you out. You know that?'

Linda's breathing began to play those tricks it had played before, down by the river. 'I rather thought you might be. Have you come to a decision?'

There was a smile in his voice. 'You are startlingly direct, my child. Well, we must change a little towards each other. You agree?'

'So far,' she replied guardedly.

'First, you must forget our relationship. I am just Luis, who wants you to be happy here. It follows that you must be more open with me, about everything! You are now quite accustomed to the Palacio, yes?'

'No, senhor.'

'But yes, you must be, because we are very used to our blue-eyed menina. So much so that it is foolish for you always to remain upstairs. For your sake I have respected the need for privacy, but it seems to me that with one so young as you we take it too far. You are to join us always for dinner, and if there should be someone you wish to invite occasionally, you just do so. And for dinner we dress up a little, no?'

'Thank you, but . . .'

'Do not say you have no friends to invite. There is Cullum, whom you call Mike; it is far better that you see him here than risk your life in that machine of his. So far, I have only invited Eve and her husband for an occasional Sunday luncheon, but there is no reason why they should not come in the evening, and there are a few others who can talk English. I will see to it that at least once a week we have the sort of company that you can really enjoy. And in return, you will try to please me by being more Portuguese when I must entertain friends who have no knowledge of the British.'

A quiver touched at Linda's lips, and a pulse throbbed a warning in her throat. 'Are you hoping to change me, senhor?'

He leant forward again, and as his glance rested upon her small fair face his smile was teasing. 'It is possible that I am. Not very much, but enough to make you understand us thoroughly.'

'You feel it is not so necessary that I be understood?'

He lifted his shoulders with good-humoured exasperation. 'Perhaps I understand you better than you think. You are appallingly young at heart, and you learned your lessons very thoroughly at Rawson Hall. Do not let us start an argument on the subject of child guidance!'

In spite of the tremors, Linda was smiling. 'If you'd give in now and then there need never be an argument. I believe there's some sort of picnic party for the children of Merida on Friday. May I take Jacinto?'

'By all means,' he said at once.

'Not to watch it from the car, but to join in?'

He eyed her quizzically. 'You may take him to see the booths and the children dancing. It will be enough.'

'That's wonderful,' she said, her eyes shining. 'I'm so grateful.'

He laughed. 'This time you will not press for more? I do not remember that you have lately demanded that we discontinue the nightly use of the thermometer.' The sudden scarlet in her cheeks answered him, and he added consideringly, 'So you begin to instruct yourself. That could be dangerous.'

'It's the only decision I've taken, senhor. I couldn't bear Jacinto to be made unnecessarily anxious about his health. I watch him closely.'

'I am sure you do. We will leave it there, Miss Grey, because in this I know I can trust you.' The arrogant head lifted. 'It is cooler today than usual, I believe. Shall we now do something about this wish you have to hike?'

'Do I really have permission to wander off?'

'We will go together—drive as far as the cork forest and walk among the trees. That will suit you?'

'Perfectly,' she said, above the absurd quickening of her heart, 'if you can spare the time.'

'We have a saying in Portugal which translated means that a man who will not make time for a pretty woman is no longer a man. I am very much a man, Miss Grey!'

'I'm convinced of it,' she murmured, and stood up with him. As they moved down towards the cedar under which the white car stood, she said, 'I don't know why it is, but these terraces always make me conscious of the age of the Palacio—much more so than the interior.'

'It is natural,' he said. 'The exterior has not changed since it was built, but ancestors of mine have left their imprint within.

So far, I myself have made few alterations, but my mother, when she came here as a bride, introduced the marble bathrooms and new kitchens, and she refurnished the small sala. It is the woman who initiates the changes.' The foreign shrug. 'It would not be her own home otherwise.'

Linda drew in her lips; the question she longed to ask remained unspoken. Instead she observed, 'I don't suppose you ever see this place objectively, as a background, but I seldom walk along the front of the Palacio without seeing horse-drawn carriages and lovely dark-eyed ladies in mantillas.'

'No men?' he asked mockingly. 'I assure you there have been many men in my family.'

'Oh, yes, there are escorts, but they all look to me like the Marquez de Filano.'

'But what a charming compliment! A Portuguese woman might say the same.'

'Far more cleverly?'

'Less obviously. She would say, "I looked at those men of the past, Luis, and I could see no features, no mouth, no eyes but yours." A subtle difference, you see?'

'And what would you reply?'

'You have imagination, Miss Grey,' he said suavely.

It was a moment of strange peril and delight. Linda felt that hand once more at her elbow as they went down the steps and crossed the path, and she wisely made no reply. At the car door he again caught sight of the bruised hand. He lifted it and touched the hurt gently with his lips, did it so naturally that he was able, the next moment, to seat her in the car and close the door with his habitual slight flourish.

He got in beside her and started the car moving out on to the drive and round the Palacio. But at the corner of the building they were stopped by a manservant who bowed and extended a letter. Luis took it and read whatever was written on it, said with more sharpness than he usually showed towards the servants,

'Who brought this?'

'A boy from the town, Senhor Marquez. He came on a bicycle to the gates and the porter brought it to me.' The man looked awkwardly towards Linda, bowed once more and stood back.

Luis tossed the letter into Linda's lap, and trod on the accelerator. They shot down the drive with incredible speed and turned right. Linda looked at the rather untidy writing, saw her own name and knew by the plunging of her heart that the letter was from Rico. For quite two or three minutes she was bereft of wits. The *idiot*, she thought furiously. Rico and his airy assumption that she could be drawn into his schemes! The sickening bad luck that his letter should arrive when it did! If it hadn't been for the fact that it would look as if she were acting for effect, she would have ripped the epistle to shreds and showered them out of the window.

'You may read your letter,' he said coldly.

'Thank you, but I'll wait.' She slipped it into her pocket. 'I hope you don't think I was expecting it.'

'Such letters are the more exciting for being unexpected, no?'

'Not to me.' She was about to add that she couldn't make out why Rico should write, when it occurred to her that he certainly wouldn't have written to her at the Palacio except about something he considered vital; she went cold.

'If you are sincere in saying that,' stated Luis, 'you will give me the letter unopened and let me deal with it.'

'That would . . . hardly be fair, would it?'

'To Rico?' His voice was polished steel. 'Rico is my concern—he is not yours! He is almost betrothed, and he has no right to communicate with you in any way. Give me the letter and forget about it.'

Linda looked despairingly out of the window, saw that he had automatically taken the turning off the main road and back on to his own land. She could feel the stiff envelope against her hip and knew an agony of indecision. Almost she could understand Luis' disgust and anger; on the other hand she couldn't let Rico down before she even knew what it was all about.

'I'm sorry,' she said weakly. 'I can't do that.'

He went on driving at a violent speed, leaving a trail of thick granite dust. They came to the cork oaks and after a minute he braked and pulled in. She looked at those long fingers as they curved tightly over the wheel, and wondered apprehensively what would come next.

Luis said crisply, 'We walk, do we not? We enjoy the coolness under the trees and you obtain that remarkable satisfaction of exercising, and discovering things about this country!'

She answered with misgiving. 'Perhaps we'd better go back to the Palacio. I'm sure you have other things to do.'

'What can be more important than instructing the young?'

He opened the door, reached Linda as she was straightening up on the grass verge. There was a cold glitter in his eyes as he asked. 'You have never before been really close to cork trees, Miss Grey? Come, then, and I will show you. But first look back across the hills. This is the best view, I always think, of the windmills which are so essential to wheat-growers in the Valle das Flores. You notice the sails are of sailcloth, not wooden slats such as you get in Holland. A fine sight, no?'

She agreed, of course. With Luis taut as whipcord at her side she would have had to agree, whatever he said. She walked mechanically and stopped when he stopped, tightened her defences against the narrowed glance which retained the glint of metal, the clipped syllables which described with utter distaste the land he loved.

'The cork is a disappointment, is it not—merely the bark of a tree which is stripped every few years. The tree is an ever-green oak, as you see by the acorns underfoot. Come with me, Miss Grey, and in a few minutes we shall see groves of trees which have been stripped only last season. They are attractive because underneath the bark the wood is a rich brown; it would make a fine timber if it were not more valuable as a source of cork.'

The walk seemed to last for ever. He stalked at her side, speaking only when he thought something should be explained. When they arrived at a clearing where the cork was stacked ready for carting, he indicated a lone house with white-washed walls where oranges and mimosa hung over into a garden where a dog snoozed.

'That is the house of my manager,' he said. 'The wife would have liked us to call for a cup of chocolate, but we will not trouble her. You have seen enough, Miss Grey?'

'Yes, thank you, senhor,' she said bleakly.

'Then we will return the way we came.'

Which they did, without exchanging another word. They met a couple of companios who sat sideways on laden donkeys and politely raised their wide felt hats many times even after the car had passed them. Farther on, near the Palacio gates, a wagonette full of very young people in scarlet and white peasant dress came jogging towards them, and Luis lifted a hand in the practised greeting. He swung the car on to the drive, stopped it between the fountain and the steps.

Again Linda made haste to get out of the car before Luis offered his hand. Too much haste, for her heels were high and caught in the hem of her dress. The material ripped, sickeningly, and she pitched forward. Her arm was gripped, she was steadied. Between vexation and humiliation her throat was too full for speech.

She went with him into the hall, faced him. He must have seen that her lashes were wet because his lips, which had parted to speak, closed suddenly. For an indecisive moment almost anything might have happened; had he made a final demand for the letter she would have handed it over at once.

But there was a faint click of heels as he bowed, nothing more. She was dismissed.

Linda went upstairs, washed and changed the dress. While she was tidying her hair Jacinto drifted in in his underwear, and when she knelt beside him to ask if he had had a good sleep, his sedate welcoming smile was tinged with surprise.

'You hold me very tight,' he said. 'I think it hurts.'

'Does it, darling? I'm sorry.'

Emotionalism with a child! Nothing was more despised at Rawson Hall. Linda rebuked herself, found his clean clothes and went with him into the bathroom. It was Jacinto's questions and the little things she had to do for him which got her through the next hour, and after that she could take him away from the Palacio for his walk, and exercise her wits for his amusement.

That evening she went down to dinner, as she had been told. Doña Velira was in the small sala with two of her old friends, and she greeted Linda with distant graciousness, and made the introduction. Obviously she had been informed that Miss Grey would now dine with the family and she had accepted it as she accepted everything Luis decreed, with an outward show of agreement.

Linda was offered sherry, was courteously asked by the guests how she liked Portugal and was told that for a girl she was muito atrevida, which meant, she gathered, that she was adventurous. She wondered how these women in black would react if she revealed the sort of things which were passing through her mind.

She looked often towards the door, listened for sounds which could never have penetrated the thick, ornate walls— the closing of the library door, a step in the hall. He would be normal this evening, urbane, excessively charming to these three old ladies. Perhaps he would come in with one of his own friends, the host who combined aloofness with geniality.

She began to think rather longingly of the meal she could have had in the nursery or in her balcony, the cigarette and a book after it.

Perhaps after all he had been too angry with her to want to see her again this evening, and for herself, Linda would have foregone the agony of sitting through dinner with him. But she had come down because she couldn't bear the idea of upsetting him again. Yes, she had to admit it; there was a mood in Luis that frightened her whenever she glimpsed it. It was a mood which made him too savagely human under the thick veneer of imperiousness and charm.

But in spite of herself she was tensed for his coming. She answered questions from the guests with the correct deferential air, readjusted the footstool for Doña Velira, rang for the servant when requested and sat stiffly in the approved Victorian manner. But all the time it was as though she were poised on a precarious rim.

'You are fond of sewing, Miss Grey?' she was asked gently.

'Oh, yes, senhora. I like it very much.'

'The embroidery?'

'A little, when I have time.'

'And do you read much?'

'About two books a week, senhora, when I can get them.'

'Como? Two books! I have a granddaughter of your age who reads perhaps two books a year.'

'Really, senhora? Perhaps I read too much, but I like it.' Was that a brief laugh out there in the hall? Linda listened, painfully.

'I do not think it is good to read a great deal, but perhaps I am out of date. We are the old ones, eh, Doña Velira?'

The empty chit-chat went on till, sip by sip, the wine glasses were emptied. There was a ponderous moment when the three ladies, with their long, aristocratic countenances and dark greying hair piled high and stabbed with jewelled combs, surveyed one another with great satisfaction. Then Doña Velira rose regally to her feet.

'We will go to dine. It is a great pity that Luis found this business appointment at the last moment, but perhaps he will come home in time to drink goodnight with us, later on.' Her voice lowered, the hooded eyes conveyed a world of meaning as she added, 'It would not surprise me to hear that this appointment of my nephew's was *private* business, with Senhor del Carros!'

Somehow Linda got through the meal, but the sense of let-down was so complete that she didn't even trouble to hide the bruised hand. However, her companions were happily intent upon the food and wine and apparently short-sighted; the meal ended with a repetition of the sighs of satisfaction.

Linda drifted back into the sala with the ladies, saw them seated and Doña Velira's footstool in place. Then she asked, politely, if she might be excused. She went back to her room, stood out on the balcony and willed herself not to conjecture about Luis' absence from the palacio this evening. It couldn't possibly have had anything to do with Linda Grey, yet she was sure, remembering his manner on the terrace, that he had intended to be here on this first occasion that she joined the family for dinner.

In the evening quiet she could hear the fountain above the music of the cicadas, the scent of roses and jasmine came up from the garden to taunt her. There was no visible moon, but its radiance glowed in a silvery arc above the distant trees. Was this loveliness eternal, she wondered, as she turned back into the room. She was arriving at a point where she would have given anything for a gale and heavy rain!

Next morning she took Jacinto to the del Carros quinta for his first sitting. It was the usual mansion filled with heavy antique furniture but delightfully tiled, and Nolette's studio was merely a bedroom which, for propriety's sake in case of visitors, had been denuded of its bed. The rest of the furniture was covered with sheets and pushed against the wall, leaving the centre of the room and all the window space free for the work table, which Nolette liked to move about, according to the light.

This morning Nolette del Carros looked businesslike in a slate-grey silk smock below which could be seen the hem of one of the usual pencil-slim skirts. The knot of hair in her nape was impeccably dark and smooth, the black wings of her eyebrows were groomed and beautiful against the creamy skin. The reddened mouth was the perfect expression of an art, the last touch of sophisticated beauty.

'For this morning, Miss Grey,' Nolette said charmingly, 'I would like to be alone with Jacinto. It is very pleasant out on the balcony, but I must close the door or the clay will dry too quickly. You do not mind?' There was no pause for Linda's reply before she tacked on, 'You will see I have put some magazines on the table out there, and it is possible to sit either in the sun or the shade, as you wish.'

With mixed feelings, Linda sank into one of the chairs. The door closed, and it must have been a good fit, for it was impossible to hear anything but the faintest murmur from within the room. For a minute or two Linda conjectured about the sort of thing such a woman as Nolette would say to Jacinto; obviously she had not wished to be overheard, even in snatches. Had Luis asked her to make friends with the boy? Or had she decided to do it smoothly, almost imperceptibly, while he sat for her?

Dispiritedly, Linda opened one of the magazines and stared at an advertisement which was identical to that of the same product in England. She read through the Portuguese wording, flipped over a few pages, and then leaned forward to look out over the neat garden surrounded by high walls and tall trees. The sun beat warmly on her head as she rested on the balcony wall, and she watched the gently-waving flowers till she became drowsy.

She saw a maid set a table under a tree and place a chair on each side of it. Senhor del Carros came out with Mike Cullum—at least, Linda deduced that the man with thick white hair and a velvet suit must be Nolette's father. Though she sat back so as not to be seen, Linda knew they talked and drank wine, nodded up towards the studio once or twice. They were apparently good friends.

The hour ended, the french door was opened. Jacinto came out blinking and Nolette was behind him, smiling down at the dark head.

'He is a good model, Miss Grey,' she said. 'Already we like each other very much. Do we not, Jacinto?'

'Yes, senhora.'

'I would like you to stay with me for lunch, my little one, but it has not been arranged. Perhaps you will more enjoy the sitting if you do not have to remain too long in this house. You will come again on Thursday, meu caro?'

'Yes, senhora.'

She placed a longish pale hand on the boy's hair, and at the sight of it Linda quivered inside. She was standing, and Nolette had come into the balcony, so that she would be behind them as they moved into the room. But near the wall the dark woman paused and looked down. Perhaps the voices

101

had drawn the two men's attention, for Linda heard Mike speak at once.

'Good morning, Nolette. How are you?'

'So it is you, Michael,' Nolette returned, smiling calmly. 'I did not think you were serious when you said you would like to watch the modelling.'

'Of course I was serious. The blueprint man always longs to watch the artist!'

'You flatter, I am afraid. If you really wish to watch you must come before noon on Thursday. Once I have started work I do not like to be interrupted.'

'I'll be here,' he promised. 'Do I have to go now?'

Nolette gave an amused shrug. 'Not if you are enjoying yourself. I will see the little Jacinto to the car and come out to you.'

'Good. If Linda's there, give her my love.'

By now, Linda was already in the room. Nolette came in, the smile still pulling at those incredible lips.

'You and Michael Cullum know each other very well, do you not?' she asked negligently.

Linda shook her head. 'No. It's merely that English people have a different approach to each other.'

'I confess I do not find Englishmen easy to understand, but I suppose it is the same with you, where our men are concerned. Tell me, Miss Grey—does it never worry you that you are now with people among whom you are unlikely to find a husband?'

'When it begins to worry me, senhora, I'll return to England.'

Carelessly, Nolette said, 'Do not leave us before we have engaged another nurse for Jacinto, will you?' And she opened the door.

With one thing and another, Linda felt quite worn as the car made its way back to the Palacio. Jacinto could find very little to say about the sitting, except that it had puzzled him when a wet cloth had been draped over the block of clay which was going to be himself.

They washed and lunched downstairs. Luis was there, with his attorney. He spoke briefly to Jacinto but his glance barely touched Linda, and she was relieved when the meal ended and she could take the boy up to his bed. She had gone without coffee, and when Jacinto was settled she decided to make herself a cup of tea. She went to her room for cigarettes, found a box of matches as well and crossed the corridor to the nursery.

She was inside the room, with the door closed behind her, before she realised that Enrico de Filano was there, springing up impatiently from the armchair near the window.

CHAPTER SEVEN

'I THOUGHT you would never come!' Rico exclaimed at once. 'What has been happening that you ignore my letter?'

'Your letter?' she echoed dazedly. 'I . . . I forgot to open it. Rico, you shouldn't be here. You know that!'

The handsome eyes were flashing feverishly, he looked imploring. 'Even though I am in the depths of uncertainty, I have remembered that you must have the excuse for my presence here. Very well, I come at this time because I know Jacinto is resting and we can talk without fear of interruptions by servants. If anyone should come I will say that I have not seen the child since his birthday and wished to give him my felicitations. It is a pity that I choose a time when he sleeps!'

'You're too glib with your excuses. For heaven's sake go. This could cause no end of trouble!'

'But it will not, because I have thought it out. I came by the back staircase, and I know this place—that there is no movement between the hours of two and four. Linda, that letter I sent you—in it, I begged you to meet me yesterday afternoon down the road. You did not come and I have been shattered by indecision. So I have to see you now. There is something only you can do for me.'

'That can't be so. I'm still a stranger here.'

'But no!' He came forward, shoulders lifted, hands thrown out in a despairing gesture. Animated, those good looks of his were devastating. 'Mike Cullum has told me that you have discovered Luis will help me if I show that I am sincere in my wish to start this plane service.'

'The Marquez did say he would. But, Rico . . .'

'Please. This is what you call death and life for me, my little pigeon. Yesterday I have a letter from this pilot friend of mine in Lisbon, who wishes us to be partners. He has met a man, a tourist who arrived in his own plane. This tourist has money and he is interested in the scheme, but he would not finance the whole of it himself. My friend has told him that I am a cousin of the Marquez de Filano, and the man is elated by the possibility of being associated with Luis in business. I can pretend to Luis that it was I who found this tourist!'

'But it wouldn't be enough,' she protested, anxious for him

in spite of the gaps in his integrity. 'After all, from Luis' angle the money is the least of it.'

'There is more, my Linda.' He was speaking so fast that every consonant was blurred. 'My friend thinks we can persuade the man to let us make a trial trip to Merida. His plane carries four passengers and their luggage. We propose to carry four passengers also, and some freight—which will have to be free of charge as we are not licensed. There are fields good enough for an experimental landing outside the town, and once we have landed we will have made out our case. You see?'

She said slowly, 'Luis doesn't doubt that you can fly. You wouldn't really prove anything.'

'I would prove the service is a good idea. And there is something else.' Rico lowered his tones, which meant that even he viewed as temerity the statement he was about to make. 'Luis has some very precious jewels in the vault of a Lisbon bank. I happen to know that he is going to have them brought here for examination before they are re-set. It is customary to transport such things in a special armoured van, but Lisbon is far from here and international thieves are everywhere.'

She couldn't help smiling. 'You've been reading thrillers! What do you propose to do—patrol the skies over the route?'

'It is not funny,' he told her fiercely. 'I am going to Lisbon to make arrangements for the transportation of the jewels by air—in the plane I have mentioned! I myself will fly them here and deliver them, less than an hour after they have left the vault in Lisbon.'

'You couldn't do it without Luis' permission!'

'We shall see. In the flying and bringing of these jewels I shall be successful—I feel it.'

'Even so, he might easily regard you as foolhardy.'

'Yes, and there is the trouble. But Luis has refused to consider this scheme chiefly because he knows my mother would not wish me to fly. This that I hope to do will prove everything to her at once.' For the first time this afternoon he managed the ravishing, disarming smile. 'You are very much a woman, Linda! Even though you are young and have the cool nature of the English, can you not imagine how a woman who thinks she has a worthless son will feel when she learns that he has brought six people, some freight and the most valuable de Filano jewels in one flight from Lisbon to Merida!'

'You'd probably give your mother a heart attack.'

'Mama is tough as old bricks! But if I tell her I can fly and show the licence from Brazil, she will not trust me. It is flying here in Portugal, doing something a little ... spectacular, which will appeal to her. If I can make her see me as a man who is above other men, she will quickly consent to the flying and be proud.' He paused, then said, 'And even if Luis thinks I am merely adventuring, at least he will have to admit that I have managed something very difficult. With my mother's consent, he must consider financing this scheme for me, once he realises it is already an accomplished fact.'

'Well, I think it's fantastic. I can't believe you're really serious!'

Rico gazed down into her eyes as if she were the only woman in the world. 'I myself am very serious, but it is as yet only a plan in my head. I am certainly going at once to Lisbon to put into operation either this plan or some other which my friend will suggest.'

'And why did you have to see me first?'

Very lightly, he touched the hair above her ear. 'Because you are my talisman in this Palacio. Luis knows my feelings, but ignores them. My mother knows nothing—and there is no one else. Someone here must be aware of what I am going to do because I need this link.'

His glance was soft as it roved her features, and she tried to shake off the feeling that she was succumbing. 'You're crazy,' she said. 'Now go, while it's still quiet.'

He shook his head. 'I have not quite finished. I believe I love you, Linda.'

'That's melodrama, but if you do, be self-sacrificing and leave me alone.'

He laughed quietly. 'What a contradiction you are! If you did not love me a little you would shout now for the servants.'

'Very well, I will!'

He held her wrist, still laughing. 'I was prepared for that. You will keep everything I have said a close secret?'

'Yes, but please go. Your mother's already anxious because you haven't been to see her for a few days, and if you were found here with me it would look terrible.'

'We have the excuse of Jacinto,' he said soothingly. 'There is one more thing I must ask you. You will not mind?'

'I'm not sure,' she said cautiously.

With a curiously boyish movement he loosened the gay silk

scarf which was tucked into the neck of his pale lavender shirt. He leaned forward slightly so that she could see the thin gold chain about his neck, and the little oval medallion in the hollow of his throat.

'My mother gave me this when I was a boy. It is usually the custom only of the middle and lower classes, but I wanted one and she bought it; I have worn it ever since.'

Touched, she said, 'Is that St Francis? I like it.'

'Before I went to Brazil I bought another, without a chain, and gave it to my mother. In Merida one does this exchanging with one's nearest kin to keep the bond during one's absence. This time it worries me that I cannot again leave it with my mother, but I will feel better if I can leave it here in the Palacio with you. Will you keep it for me, Linda?'

'Well, I . . .' She looked at the second medallion he was holding out in his palm, said desperately, 'Couldn't you give it to Juanita Montales?'

His face tightened with ludicrous horror. 'Can you understand what you are saying? It would be the most blatant form of declaration. In an hour I would find myself betrothed!'

'But, really, Rico—don't you think it would be best if you did marry the girl and forget all this airy nonsense about planes and impressing people? I can't help thinking you're going to a lot of trouble for nothing.'

His head bent forward, he tightened the cravat. 'It is not for nothing, Linda! It is for the thing I most want and I intend to try for it. Juanita is one of the reasons I must leave Merida for a while.'

'I don't think you've given her a fair trial.'

'What do they say?' he murmured cheerfully. 'You can take a horse to the well but you cannot make him eat? I am sorry, but I have no appetite for Juanita.' He pressed the little gold medallion into her hand and closed her fingers over it. 'Keep it for me and give it to me next time we meet.'

'Are you going to see your mother?' she asked quickly.

'I will do it now—go to her room and tell her I may be away with friends for a few days. She will think only of Portão.'

'Then couldn't I pretend to find this thing in the corridor or somewhere, and give it to her?'

He considered this, then shook his head. 'She is superstitious, and might regard my losing it as an omen. I do not want her to be in the least disturbed, so that when I land the plane she will have no need to be anything but joyful. You have faith in me, Linda?'

She sighed, half exasperated. 'You'll get through, but I'm not sure how. Are you travelling to Lisbon by road?'

'Yes, with a man who goes there on business early tomorrow morning.'

'Then I think you'll return in the same way,' she said flatly. 'Will you be away long?'

'It will take some time—perhaps a week, perhaps a month. You wish me much luck?'

With her hand on the doorknob she answered, 'I wish you much sanity, Rico.'

She opened the door and looked along the deserted corridor, then beckoned to him. He passed close to her in the doorway, lightly kissing her forehead and stifled his laughter when she jerked backwards. With exaggerated caution he tiptoed along the corridor and at the bend he looked back and waved nonchalantly. With relief, Linda closed herself once more within the nursery.

Almost without thinking she switched on the kettle and took the teapot from the cupboard. She spooned tea into the cold pot and was on the point of pouring lukewarm water before her wits asserted themselves. She set the pot on the table, sank down into a chair.

Rico was incorrigible. He couldn't possibly get far with this idea, but because it did hold the germ of success he had to try it. Apparently he wasn't in the least dismayed by the prospect of flying a strange plane and trying to land it on one of the fields near Merida, but then the owner might feel differently about allowing him to do so. Perhaps when Rico got together with his friend and the tourist they would think up some less flimsy plan. For his sake, she hoped something good would come out of their meeting together in Lisbon; when a man who had never done anything really worthwhile found himself tingling at last with an ambition, it did seem that he ought to be accorded a few lucky breaks.

It was minutes later, when she was drinking her second cup of tea, that Linda realised, with a qualm, that if anything did go wrong she would be implicated. Still, she could never have stopped Rico except by spilling everything he trusted her to keep to herself. After all, being forced into the role of a confidante doesn't make one responsible for another's escapades. The best thing was to forget it; it might be days, or even weeks, before Rico could act, and by that time others would have added their knowledge and common sense to the venture. So much so that it might never come off!

The rest of that day passed with almost uncanny quietness. The attorney came to dinner, this time with his wife, and Nolette turned up with her father at about nine-thirty. She had felt, she said, that she must call and tell Luis that Jacinto was the perfect model; she had never enjoyed an hour with a child so much in her life. Ten minutes later Linda said a formal goodnight and went up to her room.

And perhaps because Nolette had just reminded everyone of her elegant existence, Linda thought of those jewels in a bank vault in Lisbon, the jewels which Luis intended to have re-set—for Nolette, probably. Nolette, the woman who had loved him six years ago but gone away because he had been promised for a long time to someone else. Luis had kept his word to the wraith-like Amalia and waited till he was fairly sure he was the reason Nolette had remained unmarried before inviting her back to Merida. It had all been carried out with rigid regard for propriety.

The days went by. On Wednesday there was a drive with Mike Cullum; the studio on Thursday, with Mike present and talking sculpture with Nolette while she worked on the clay chin and jaw. And on Thursday night Nolette came to dine at the Palacio, the only guest and made much of by Doña Velira. On Saturday, Nolette came again, but true to his promise Luis had also invited the Bayes and Mike Cullum, and two Portuguese couples who talked good English. There was music and a little dancing, strolling in the moonlit gardens and a nightcap on the terrace.

At meal times Rico was occasionally mentioned, but it seemed to have been accepted that he was spending the time with young friends in the vicinity of Portão, and as he had never been a good correspondent no one was perturbed that he did not write.

Doña Velira went over by invitation to see the Montales, and one afternoon the girl, Juanita, came for tea with her mother. She was pretty and apparently unexciting, but Linda knew that the demure exterior could be deceptive. She recalled the children's fair to which she had taken Jacinto for an hour or two, the quiet young ladies who had formed up for a dance and suddenly seemed to go mad to the rhythm of guitars. Still, Juanita was of a more exalted family than they; not for

109

anything would she have been seen dancing at a fair.

Jacinto, Linda had to admit, had been bored by the dancing and the booths, the smells of drying foods and the laughing children. Too much going on all at once, she guessed. But for several days afterwards he had reminded Linda about the puppet dolls and the small merry-go-round, the chute with a sandpit at the bottom and the little painted boats on the river.

'Next time we go to one of those picnics,' she promised him, 'we'll row in one of the boats and you must try the chute. Some children have a sandpit in their own garden.'

'What do they do with it?' he asked curiously.

She thought of the mites at children's homes in England, their blissful faces as they heaped sand into a battered bucket, or buried their toes, or simply squelched handfuls of the precious stuff. No explaining it to a child; he'd have to experience it. But would he ever get joy even from a sandpit if he had to play there without other children? In his sheltered loneliness he was pathetic.

There came a day when it rained quite heavily for two or three hours, and on the following day it was cool and clear. The rainwashed grass and bushes were startling in their greenness, and flowers which had seemed to be approaching the end of their season started budding all over again. The revitalising of the growth had happened quickly, as it does in hot countries, and Linda was enchanted with it.

She took Jacinto out straight after breakfast, and together they counted the buds on the roses, the new flower spikes pushing up out of the carnations. They had reached a group of geraniums when Luis came out.

He crossed the grass and stood above them. 'Good morning, little ones. You look for butterflies?'

They both got up, and Linda said, 'Everything's growing again. I suppose the valley will fill up with new flowers?'

'There are flowers in the valley all the year round. In winter the wild red gladiolus, narcissi and the vines; for the rest of the year everything blooms most of the time.' He paused. 'I have to see an old friend of our family this morning. He has a small fruit farm which may interest you. I can wait for ten minutes if you are not ready.'

She said carefully, in the cool tones she had found helpful just lately, 'Perhaps you would really prefer to take Jacinto alone, senhor.'

'Perhaps I would, Miss Grey,' he said with a sharp smile,

'but on this occasion I think you must come too. Are you ready?'

She nodded and said, 'Yes. We'll wait here for the car.'

Five minutes later they were on their way, with Linda sitting as she had sat before, with Jacinto on her knee. As there was no immediate attempt at conversation, she looked out of the window at the vine-gardens and olive trees which lined the road down past Merida and out on to a valley road she had not travelled before.

Since that afternoon when Linda had refused to yield up Rico's letter, the matter had not again been referred to between herself and Luis. When Doña Velira had announced the following evening that Rico was off for some sport with his friends, Luis had flickered a glance towards Miss Grey as though he was aware she must already know this fact, but his aloofness then and afterwards had saved Linda from feeling guilty, and now the episode with Rico in the nursery was becoming remote and unimportant; she didn't doubt that he would show up one day with his problem still unresolved.

Luis turned the car into a by-road between peach trees, and within a few minutes the farmhouse became visible, a flat-roofed dwelling with striped shades over the window and a side patio covered with flowering climbers.

Luis spoke to the child. 'You remember Dom Josef, pequeno? You have seen him once, I think, when he came to lunch with us, but it was some time ago.'

'I do not remember, Papa.'

'No matter, you will like him very much.' To Linda, he explained, 'Dom Josef was a professor at the university, but he is now retired. He lives alone here among his fruit trees, but he has a married daughter in Merida, and he also has several hobbies, so he is not lonely.'

He drove round the short gravel path and stopped near the shallow steps. He came round and helped them out, and by the time the car door had closed Dom Josef was in the porch, bowing ceremoniously and totally unconscious of the small black beret perched on the top of his silvery hair. He smilingly acknowledged the introduction to Miss Grey and bent to shake hands with Jacinto.

It seemed to be understood that they would not go into the house. Dom Josef led the way round to the patio, where bright-coloured wooden chairs were arranged round a table and he saw them seated and called for wine and glasses of

111

chocolate. Obviously he was overjoyed at the honour of receiving the Marquez, but it seemed that Luis had called here quite recently, for the plump old housekeeper who brought the loaded tray referred to it with pride. She also said, 'It is today, senhor?' and received a nod from her employer.

Linda and Jacinto drank their chocolate and Luis complimented Dom Josef on the wine. They talked of the forthcoming peach harvest, of the enlargement of the little canning factory in Merida, of the flower festa which would take place in a few days. Dom Josef, it seemed, had promised thousands of blossoms which would convert one of the boats into a crinolined lady; his daughter would be in charge of the work of art and already she was practising with paper rosettes on the framework.

It was Jacinto who first saw the puppies. At the end of the patio was a rustic trellis constructed of thin gnarled logs, and at the base between the pink roses which festooned the trellis he caught small movements. He stared, leaned back to stare harder, and that was when Linda's attention was drawn to the same spot. She saw the puppies plainly, two small, tubby brown ones with squashed black noses and ridiculous tails; as she looked a third was pushed along near the trellis by a plump brown hand.

Quickly she looked at Luis, but he was talking to the old man, lifting his shoulders in the foreign way he had and half smiling. Both men had their backs to the trellis, yet it seemed impossible that they could not be conscious of the mounting excitement within Jacinto. The child slipped down from his chair and clasped his fingers over the edge of the table, waiting in anguish till there should be a lull in the conversation. It came at last. Dom Josef bent towards him.

'You want something, senhorito?'

'Dogs,' breathed Jacinto. 'Cachorrinhos. They come into the patio!'

'Dogs?' echoed Dom Josef in surprise, and he feigned short sight as he turned and glanced towards the back of the house. 'Those funny things are dogs, you tell me?'

Jacinto saw through this. He gave an excited laugh. 'May I touch them?'

'But yes, if your papa consents.'

Jacinto's eyes were enormous as he looked at Luis. Luis' head nodded, he rose as Linda got up to accompany the child,

112

and sat down again to continue the talk. He was apparently totally uninterested in the puppies.

Jacinto, sitting on a step at the edge of the paved patio with one puppy in his arms and another captured between his shoes, was too utterly enchanted to speak. Linda sat beside him and stroked the third furry bundle. She was afraid to say much to the child because his agony of bliss might so easily be shattered, but at length she persuaded him to put the three puppies together and watch their antics. One would stray, and the child would leap up and place him back with his brothers. He let them nibble his fingers, instinctively tapped the nose of one which bit too hard. He pushed a hand over his hot face and left a smear on his forehead, could not resist sweeping one of the wriggling bodies up close to him. The other two were climbing over each other in Linda's lap, and Luis chose that moment to stroll across with Dom Josef to look down upon them.

'So you find playmates, you two,' he said calmly. 'I am afraid you cannot stay here with these things all day. What do you suggest we should do?'

Jacinto rocked slightly with the puppy in his arms. Linda couldn't bear the aching need in him. She set down the two puppies and pushed herself up on to her feet, found herself on the step above the patio and therefore able to look straight into Luis' dark eyes. They were enigmatic, but he said pleasantly, 'Well, Miss Grey, what would you suggest?'

But Dom Josef must have been touched by the child's silent imploring. He cut short the scene. 'We tease you, Jacinto,' he said. 'I think the Senhor Marquez will let you have one of the puppies.'

Relief surged through Linda, but through emotion her smile was crooked. 'You see, darling, you have your puppy! Isn't that wonderful?'

'It is wonderful,' he agreed fervently.

'That was such a charming letter you wrote me before your birthday,' said Luis. 'I had to do something about it, but there were no puppies to be had except these of Dom Josef's, and they were too young to leave their mother. So we had to wait till now.'

Jacinto was honest. 'It was Linda who wrote the letter,' he said.

'So? But I was sure it was your writing!'

113

'Papa, you know I cannot write yet.'

'Yes, I do. Was the wish also Linda's?'

'No, we both wish for a puppy.'

'Then we must have two puppies, no? You will have one each, and they will not get lonely in the kennel. You can spare two, Dom Josef?'

'Certainly, senhor. The mother will like to keep one of them with her, but I will be very happy for you to have the others. Choose yours, Jacinto.'

The little boy stood up, his eyes glazed with happiness. 'I have it,' he said.

'And for you, senhorita,' said Dom Josef, bending to pick up the puppy which was sleepily spread over the toe of her sandal, and gallantly presenting it to her, 'the puppy seems to have chosen you. With my compliments!'

'Thank you, Dom Josef.'

With the third puppy in the crook of his arm, the old man accompanied them to the car. Jacinto was put into the back, where he found a rug for the puppies, and Linda took her usual seat in front. There were more thanks, both for the puppies and for Dom Josef's hospitality, and Luis drove down again between the peach trees and on to the road.

Linda said, 'You've made Jacinto very happy, senhor.'

'And you?' he asked. 'How do you feel about this small success?'

'Exceedingly grateful. And it isn't so small. I do wish you'd told me this treat was in store for Jacinto.'

'Why?' with sarcasm. 'Would it have made you like me better and trust me?'

He couldn't know how foolish the question was. She made no attempt to answer it, but said, 'Did you hear Jacinto laugh when he first ran towards the puppies?'

'I did not notice it particularly, but perhaps I am less sensitive to his reactions than you are. To me he has always been a small boy for whom I am responsible and for whom I naturally have an affection because he is mine. I am by no means a doting parent.'

'I've been aware of that, of course.'

'And being curious, you have wondered,' he stated evenly. 'You have no doubt decided that I am incapable of loving a woman, let alone a child.'

Linda's heart began to knock. She looked over her shoulder

114

at the completely oblivious Jacinto, clasped her hands rather damply in her lap.

'You're the most capable man I know,' she said. 'Your . . . your love affairs aren't my concern.'

'I have no love affairs,' he said abruptly. 'A love affair takes two people who have a desperate need for each other. Together, they are conscious of no one else, and apart there is only the flaming necessity to be together again.' A pause. 'Do you remember telling me that you do not care for the Portuguese type of love?'

'Yes, I remember,' she replied thinly. 'I was thinking of marriage, not affairs.'

'Your opinion has not changed?'

Linda moistened her lips, grateful that he had to look ahead most of the time. 'I don't know,' she said. 'I only know that I wouldn't want to be chosen by someone's parents as a suitable bride for their son.'

He shrugged offhandedly. 'But there is a great deal to be said for two young people coming together with the idea of loving each other and marrying. At least they are spared the pains of uncertainty, the spears of jealousy.'

Linda quivered. She remembered, suddenly, that Nolette had regularly reported Mike's presence in her studio while she worked on the bust of Jacinto. Was it possible that no real understanding existed between Luis and Nolette, or was their relationship so tenuous that Nolette had to prod him gently with the mention of Mike, with whom she had her art in common? Linda couldn't imagine Luis being jealous of a man like Michael Cullum, but then jealousy was illogical and it could spring up almost anywhere. If Luis was jealous, he must be in love.

They swept up the drive to the Palacio, the car stopped and Jacinto, with a puppy in each arm, was extracted from the back seat. He stood swaying ecstatically on the terrace till Luis said the puppies must be taken round to the back and kept in the kennel which was already set there.

'And these spaniels, or whatever they are, must be properly trained and kept in the wire enclosure except when you are walking them. You understand?' he said. 'They are the responsibility of you and Linda.'

Jacinto beamed dazedly. 'Graças, Papa,' he said. 'Thank you many times!'

115

But if Luis had gained pleasure from humouring the child, it seemed now to have evaporated. He escorted them along the terrace, inclined his head to Linda and entered the Palacio by the first door.

The puppies created a mild sensation in the kitchens and were spoken of a little severely at lunch time by Doña Velira, but they had come to stay and were now therefore part of Jacinto's world. He went to sleep with a smile on his lips, and he awoke asking about them. Discipline the child took in his stride, and when Linda pointed out that little dogs needed training if they were to grow up into lovable big dogs, and that training was the opposite of spoiling, Jacinto understood at once, and was willing to do his share.

That afternoon, though, he spent most of the usual walk period inside the wired enclosure. Watching him, Linda knew he had never been so happy in his life. He was tired early that evening, and after he was in bed she had time to write a belated letter home.

Previously she had enlarged upon the strictness of the household, so it was easy to fill a page or two with today's unexpected relaxation of the code. But when she had finished writing about the puppies there was nothing else to say. She thought of her father and Charlotte in their modern flat, the semi-bohemians who were Charlotte's friends. She recalled parties at which women wore blue jeans and brightly coloured sweaters trimmed with diamanté, and she felt farther away than ever from her own people. The letter ended lamely, but she knew it was unlikely they would notice it; she scribbled a last line about it being time to get ready for dinner with the 'nobs', and left it at that.

She put on a wide-necked patterned dress which was predominantly blue, gave her hair the usual attention and made up her face. As she walked along the corridor she wondered why each evening at this time she had the sensation of uneasiness blended with excitement. Perhaps it was because she never knew who would be down there in the small sala, taking a drink before dinner. There was mostly a guest or two, sometimes several, and she always knew by the way her heart reacted just before she entered whether Luis was in the room. Tonight it gave a faint flop, and sure enough only Doña Velira was in there, seated in state with her feet raised, and holding a glass of deep red wine in the bony fingers that glittered with rings.

'Sit down, Miss Grey,' she was bidden graciously. 'Ring for the servant if you wish for wine.'

'No wine, thank you, senhora.'

Linda sat, and waited. Doña Velira drank with relish, held the half-empty glass in front of her and regarded the fair young face with her fading brown eyes. Her foot, in a delicate black kid slipper, tapped gently on the stool, her eyelids came down once or twice in their usual fashion, like shutters. She had that familiar look of a benign yet deadly eagle.

'I believe it is you we have to thank for the dogs, Miss Grey. My nephew consents, so I have nothing against it. But next time you have one of these clever ideas I wish you to come to me before you do anything else. You understand?'

'Yes, senhora.'

'I have already told you that I am dissatisfied with your methods of teaching the child. Do not make it that I must complain about other things also.'

'Very well, senhora.'

'There is something else, which has nothing to do with the boy. I want your word that this will be between us—quite secret.'

Linda was astonished but too low-spirited to bother very much. 'Of course,' she said politely. 'You have my word.'

But Doña Velira was not quite so sure of herself as she appeared. She finished her wine and set the glass on the table beside her, locked her fingers so tightly that the rings looked painful on the old ivory fingers. 'Miss Grey, you know the hopes of all of us regarding Nolette del Carros and the Senhor Marquez. Quite certainly Nolette returned to Merida because she felt her place was here at the Palacio as Luis' wife, but she has been back more than two weeks, she has seen him almost daily, and nothing has been announced or even hinted at. This is not the fault of Luis, but of Nolette.'

'Oh.' For the life of her, Linda could not have said more just then. She looked at Doña Velira, saw that under the grand manner she was genuinely disturbed. Actually, she must be really shaken, to confide in the negligible Miss Grey. But in a minute or two the matter became clearer.

'I am surmising only,' the senhora went on. 'Luis has said nothing, but he is becoming intolerant in small things, and

117

occasionally he has even spoken with a faint sharpness to me. He cares much for Nolette, and when she arrived it seemed she cared for him. But she has changed in this short time, and perhaps you can guess why.'

'You mean . . . Mr Cullum?'

The other's eyes narrowed. 'So you have seen something? You must tell me.'

'No, there's been nothing, beyond the usual friendship between two people with similar interests. Mike enjoys watching in the studio, but I don't think there's more to it than that. Senhorita del Carros asks his opinion and they talk shop, that's all. At least, that's all I've ever seen. I don't think she can possibly be growing fond of Mike; he's not her sort at all, really.'

Doña Velira's foot tapped again. 'There is something, Miss Grey. Nolette is not to be measured by other Portuguese women. She has lived in Madrid and Paris, she has mixed with all kinds of people and has grown away from us to some extent. I must confess that myself I see very little in Mr Cullum; he is a pleasant man and knows much about buildings, but he is not a positive character like my nephew . . . or even my son! However, for Nolette he may have something—this knowledge of architecture and sculpture, perhaps. But it cannot happen; it must not. My nephew's happiness is very precious to me, and I know the future will be insupportable to him if he cannot have Nolette. You are English and so is Mr Cullum. Can you speak to him about this?'

Linda's heart was like lead, but she was startled. 'Good heavens, no! If there's anything between Mike and Nolette I'm not likely to have any influence, and if there isn't, it's unnecessary to approach him.'

'I agree. I asked because I am not too sure of your ways with each other. Well, there can be only one remedy. Luis invites Mr Cullum here for you, does he not? Do you like the man?'

Oh, no, thought Linda faintly; not this! 'He's . . . quite good fun,' she admitted.

'He would spend more time with you if you asked him?'

'Would you expect a Portuguese girl to run after a man at your bidding?'

An expressive shrug. 'That is different. You two are English and it is quite usual for the English of both sexes to see much of one another in private. I am not asking you to be indiscreet. It is simply this. You must show more interest in Mr Cullum, do your best to keep him away from Nolette. If he is in the studio, draw him out with you when you leave. When he comes here, monopolise him. A man of his kind will respond to flattery, and Nolette is too Portuguese not to be affronted if he transfers his attentions. She will turn to Luis.'

'Don't you think that all three of them are old enough to know what they're up to?'

Normally, Doña Velira would have been infuriated by such a tone from an inferior. Just now, however, she was on a single track and not to be diverted.

'When things are very close to my heart, Miss Grey,' she said slowly, 'I am not squeamish. For you, this will be easy and it need not last for long. Be more friendly with Mr Cullum, and soon he will talk of Nolette and you will be able to gather how matters are between them. But do not let him or anyone else suspect that we have discussed this. I am not asking you to do this for me, but for Luis who has been good to you.'

She spoke the final word as the door opened to admit her daughter and son-in-law. Linda sat very still and watched the greetings, the serving of more wine. From their exchanges she learned that Luis was out tonight, and she thought, a little wildly, that as soon as dinner was over she would be able to get away and think.

But she was thinking now, chaotically, about Luis who wanted Nolette, and Nolette who had turned down proposals while waiting for Luis but who might be just a scrap attracted by Mike.

She recalled Luis' remark about jealousy and uncertainty, the sternness which had come into his expression and remained there. Could she do this for Luis? Did she . . . love him enough?

The last question was still unanswered when she went to bed that night.

CHAPTER EIGHT

THE flower festa of Merida was rather different from the usual riot of dancing, singing and eating, the buying of charms and potions, toys and trinkets. It seemed that invariably at this time of the year the Valle das Flores was at its most glorious, and to give thanks for the fertility of fields and gardens, the people first gathered for an immense service outside the church and afterwards made their way to the river, where the decorated barges floated by. There was dancing in the evening, of course, because no festa could be complete without it.

It seemed that it was usual for the Marquez to make an appearance on the river bank about midday, and for him to look in on the dancing for an hour in the evening, but Doña Velira hadn't witnessed the spectacle for years, and many of the rich families viewed a little of the proceedings from their cars and considered they had done their duty. However, they were not missed by the gay throngs of Merida.

Linda was asked one lunch-time whether she would like to be free on the festa day, and before she could answer Doña Verlia had mentioned that she would be only too pleased to have care of the little one whilst Linda was away; would not the good Mr Cullum act as her escort? As Mike happened to be there at the table with them, the outcome of this manoeuvre was inevitable.

'Why, that's grand, Linda!' he said cheerfully. 'We'll both be raw enough to get the best out of it. Any time limit, Luis? I mean, can Linda have the whole day?'

'She will need lunch and a rest during the afternoon,' Luis answered evenly. 'There is a long break between the morning's procession along the river and the festivities of the evening.'

'All the better,' Mike pronounced. 'I'll get a picnic ready, and we may get as far as the Gruta de Santa Maria.' He turned to Linda. 'You did say you'd like to see the source of the river some time.'

'Yes, I would,' she said quietly.

Luis made no comment, and Mike took his silence as consent.

Thus it was that on the morning of the flower festa, under a brilliant sky, Mike drove his small black car up to the Palacio, met Linda at the fountain and saw her comfortably set in the seat beside his own. It was eleven o'clock, the time at which the flower procession along the river was scheduled to start, but when they reached the popular viewing spot on the river bank there were hundreds of sightseers, but as yet no sights to see. Except, of course, the family picnic parties, the women selling charms for charity, the village girls in their black skirts and gaily striped aprons, the men in bright slacks and shirts, the impatient children and the padre on his motor-scooter.

The procession of flowery barges came in sight at last, and for about an hour they followed a routine. From the bend in the river, each barge approached separately, poled along by a smiling young man in black knee-breeches, a flowing silk shirt and a hat covered with blossoms. The first was an immense cushion of roses with a senhorita's face laughing from its centre, and the second the vast crinoline manufactured by Dom Josef's daughter—a remarkable affair this, with tiers of pink and white roses to the waist, a pure white bodice and a braid of scarlet buds about the skirt; the girl who wore it tilted a lovely black head covered by a juliet cap of the same scarlet rosebuds.

There was a gigantic swan in white camellias, a flowered throne and chairs graced by the flower queen and princesses, a white tree under which nymphs played, a barge full of children in clothes made entirely of flowers, and lastly a fine replica of the church in wild flowers from the valley. The whole time the procession was on the move there were small canoes near the bank from which young men pelted the onlookers with flowers while some of their companions played guitars and sang fados.

As Mike said, 'They're going mad in the midday sun, but they'll have the good sense to go to bed this afternoon and sleep it off. Seen enough, Linda?'

She nodded, but looked back as she followed Mike, who was pushing a way for them through the crowd. The ground rose, and from one spot she could see several of the barges strung out like magnificent birds along the river. Flowers floated on the surface of the water and blooms were still sailing through the air.

Someone said, 'Mangericão, senhorita?' and offered a pot of basil.

Mike laughed. 'Want it, Linda? No unmarried girl should be without her little green plant.'

121

He paid, and ceremoniously placed the small black pot with its tiny but healthy plant in her hands. She knew some of the properties associated in Portugal with a pot of basil. In Merida it had to be given by a young man, and the girl could convey with carnations various messages that the maidenly tongue was too shy to voice.

They were in the car and moving when she asked, 'What's the exact formula with these pots of basil? A maid at the Palacio once told me very sadly that although she had been given one of them she had never been able to stick anything but a white carnation in among the leaves. I didn't like to probe, but I was curious.'

'I'm not too clear about it myself, but I believe white is a sort of negative, pink is said to be for awakening love, those speckled ones for uncertainty, and the scarlet, of course, for the genuine heart-throb. There are other colours in between which have various shades of meaning, but that's roughly the idea. A girl can make what she feels fairly plain without actually committing herself.'

'It's a pretty custom,' Linda said. 'I like the simplicity of the country people.'

'But the educated are not quite so simple,' Mike commented. 'Look at Rico and his Juanita!'

Linda smiled, and bent down to lodge the pot of basil safely near her feet. 'Put yourself in his place. How would you feel if someone picked out a girl for you and expected you to fall in love with her?'

'Rather relieved, I think. I'm definitely the marrying type, and I don't seem too good at picking 'em myself. In any case, Rico's grown up with that kind of thing and Juanita's all right, from what I've seen of her. By the way, have you heard anything from him?'

'Nothing at all.'

'No one else has, either, but the general impression is that he's gone off for a month's wild oats because once his engagement is announced he'll have to sober up. At heart, you know, he's a model son.'

'Even a model son can have inclinations and ambitions which don't coincide with those his family have for him. No one has tried to help him a scrap.'

'Helping a chap to take to the air is a bit tricky. Far better for him to get a job with some impersonal airline and save his ambitions till he can afford them. Even Rico has a quota of the de Filano arrogance. He has to be part owner of whatever he goes in for, never an employee.'

Just then Linda forgot Rico, for they were passing the spot to which Luis had brought Jacinto and herself on the little boy's birthday. She looked down towards the river and picked out the tree under which they had stood. She remembered Jacinto running up the bank and prodding with a twig at the earth, her own wilting moment of self-knowledge; and she remembered thinking on that day that with luck she would go to the Gruta de Santa Maria with Luis. But she was on her way there with Mike.

The road wound on, always above the river. It ran through miles of flowers and stunted olives, through a cypress wood and out of it on to a hillside where a village straggled and a pink-washed church rested somnolently under the beating sun. They passed from the edge of the Valle das Flores into the country beyond, and Linda told herself that she ought to feel free and uplifted.

For a while they talked of the vineyards and flower farms, the river which now lay far below them, a thread of writhing green growth at the bottom of a natural bowl. Then the river widened into a long narrow lake, which petered away among trees and bushes. Mike brought the car round into a grassy lane, they jolted along it till it ended at a small clearing. He switched off the engine, and immediately Linda became aware of the gurgling of waters. They were very close to the river and not so far from its rocky source.

'Come on,' said Mike. 'It's quite a traipse. Do you mind?'

'Of course not. All good things should be difficult to get at.'

'They are, believe me,' he told her, 'and you find so many good things too late. I'll go first where it's narrow.'

They went down to a river which bounced shallowly among the rocks and kept beside it on a footpath. Quite soon Mike had to go ahead and cling to tree roots as the ground sloped upwards, leaving the river to their left in a small chasm. There were tiny waterfalls at the side of the road which drained out on to the path, and a rickety bridge which, Mike suggested, should hold out for a day or two longer; it was certainly hair-raising to cross it above those shallow rushing waters. They climbed again, could not see the river for a few minutes, and then the footpath ended at an enchanting glade set about a small waterfall which bubbled straight out of the rocks.

Linda stood quite still in the cool dimness. There were ferns and saplings, some little blue flowers known as Mary's-hood among the lush grasses, a pool below the river's source, and still the sound of the unseen waterfall which created the hurried waters of the river. And just above the worn rocks where the river began, a cross had been beautifully carved in the stone.

'It's kept clear of moss,' observed Mike. 'I believe there's some legend attached to this place.'

'Luis told me that people bring their problems here on their saint's day, and have them solved.'

'I'll bet he doesn't believe in it himself. I don't suppose he's ever been floored by a problem in his life.'

Linda remembered the rather one-sided talk with Doña Velira. 'Not floored, perhaps, but he has a few troubles, I believe.' She lingered, wondering if there could be some magic in this atmosphere; if so, she ought to use it. She sat on a lichened stone and looked about her, said with apparent irrelevance, 'Mike, don't you think Nolette del Carros is taking the dickens of a while to finish that head of Jacinto?'

Mike was never surprised by a sudden change of topic. He picked a piece of lime-green fungus from a tree-trunk and said casually, 'Maybe she's a slow worker, and she's certainly a perfectionist. She doesn't work on the thing between sittings, and I believe she said that a head mostly takes ten or a dozen. She did some other artist in a dozen sittings.'

'But Jacinto is only a smooth-faced little boy.'

'The result has to please Luis, and believe me, that's not easy! Has someone been beefing about the time she's spending on it?'

She shook her head. 'Even Jacinto doesn't grumble, but that's possibly because she's so sweet to him.' She paused, then asked, 'Don't you get bored with watching the clay modelling?'

'She's too good at it ever to be boring. Years ago I did a bit of it myself as a hobby, and while watching her I've realized that my whole approach was cockeyed. I feel very lucky to be in Merida at the same time as Nolette.'

'Is she that good?'

'It isn't that she's a creative genius, because personally I don't think she's quite got Jacinto.' He added hastily, 'I'll deny it if you quote that! I've really no authority to pass an opinion. I'm a hack and she's an artist; I've a hack's respect for everything she turns out. After you'd taken Jacinto off yesterday Nolette asked if I'd like her to do a head of me.'

Linda looked at him curiously, saw nothing except Mike, with his slightly jaded expression and the incipient stoop of the shoulders. 'What did you answer?'

He shrugged. 'I thought it was safe to assume she was joking. That sort of of compliment is above me.'

'You're modest, Mike.'

'I try, honey,' he said with a grin. Then he shivered, theatrically. 'Let's get out again in the sunshine. Are you hungry?'

'Fairly. What did you bring?'

'I've no idea. It'll be a voyage of discovery for both of us. I'll go first again.'

It must have been nearly two when they got back to the clearing and opened the picnic basket. Linda spread the cloth and revealed the contents of the tins. There were legs of chicken, stuffed tomatoes, small crayfish salads, pãozinhos—those crisp golden rolls—and butter, some fruit, cheese and flasks of coffee. They both took a long time over lunch, and lay back happily after it, smoking lazily as they looked up through the branches at the glimpses of a warm blue sky.

'You know something?' Mike said as he gently blew smoke and watched it disintegrate. 'Luis didn't want me to take you out today. The noble Marquez doesn't care for me.'

Linda's nerves tightened. 'I don't think it's as simple as that. As a man, I think he'd find it quite easy to like you very much.'

'Have I slipped up somewhere?'

'Only you can answer that. There's Nolette, of course.'

Mike digested this, raised his head and gave her an astonished look. 'Dash it,' he said, 'Nolette isn't one of your Juanita types. She's been used to a full life; he won't be able to shut her up in his palace when they're married! What's wrong with my kicking around on the fringe of her life while I'm here? We learn from each other.'

With studied casualness she asked of the sky, 'Only about architecture and sculpture?'

He got right up on his elbow and looked at her unbelievingly. 'I'd love to think you're jealous,' he said, 'but I know you're not. And Luis is not only above such emotions—they just don't enter his orbit. No, there's some other reason he dislikes me.'

125

'If he disliked you he wouldn't invite you to the Palacio.'

'I'm invited for your benefit—didn't you know that? He thinks you're a marvel with Jacinto and he wants to keep you there. Yesterday he asked me when my holiday ends.'

There could be a very obvious reason for that, thought Linda. 'And when does it end?' she queried.

'I'm not in a hurry. I've had some stuff sent over from my office and I can do the preliminary work on a couple of contracts right here in Merida. I can hang on for several weeks.'

'Do you want to?'

He lay back again, took his cigarette from his lips and pressed it down into the earth beside him. 'I don't know. There are times when I feel I can't face London ever again, and other times when I think I'd feel a heap better if I were working. To my annoyance, I've discovered that where my emotions are concerned I'm even more of a chump than I imagined.'

She laughed. 'Do you often think of that girl you lost?'

'Hardly at all, but something she stirred up refuses to go back to sleep. I think that's why I go so often to the del Carros' house. Nolette is a pretty absorbing person to be with, and watching her at work gives me plenty to think about afterwards. Then again, she's dark and restrained, she has that husky foreign voice and she's good enough to be interested in my work. She's so entirely different from my late lamented that I find her a wonderful tonic.'

Linda said non-committally, 'So long as you remember this is Portugal.'

'You sound like Eve. When she came down last weekend she warned me off Nolette because Luis might not care to have me calling there. She also warned me off you.'

'Me? How do I come into it?'

'Well, you wouldn't stay with the de Filanos if you married, would you? They want to keep you, sweetie.' He added lightly, 'But don't worry. I'll marry you any time you feel you can face it.'

'Why, thanks,' she said composedly.

'In fact,' he sounded a little moody, 'I'm sure I'd be far better off with someone like you. Have I told you that before?'

'Several times.'

'The trouble is, I'm weak-kneed over women. And where's the woman who'll put up with that?'

'Where indeed? I can only suggest you wear a pair of mental slacks to hide the mental weak knees.'

'That's an idea. You know, Linda, it could be awfully bad for you to stay on here indefinitely.'

'Could it?'

'You must see that yourself. You're not the type to grow into a little old nanny in a foreign country. You need a husband and youngsters of your own—or you will do, very soon. Do you realise what will happen if you stay here?'

'Yes,' she said slowly, 'I think I do.'

But Mike had already decided to put it into words. 'You'll have Jacinto alone for another year or so, and then there'll probably be more children—Nolette's.' Linda made no reply, and he went on. 'You have to prepare yourself for that, or get out.' He paused, and when there was still no comeback, he said, rather carefully, 'I'd hate to think you were . . . aching for something you couldn't have.'

She did answer him then. 'Your voice is awfully soothing, Mike. I was nearly asleep. What were you saying?'

'Okay,' he said resignedly. 'I'll mind my own business. But if you ever need a get-out I'm with you all the way.'

After which they both dozed for a long time. For so long, in fact, that their small clearing began to darken and a late afternoon breeze fanned them into wakefulness. They stretched cheerfully, put away the picnic basket and set out for Merida.

The dancing in the market square of the town that evening was interesting to watch for a while but hardly a type into which a stranger could enter. Mike grew tired of the strutting and swirling, the fast yet plaintive strumming, and he suggested they go on to Portão and take in dinner at the Estrella.

On their return from the river Linda had washed and tidied at Eve's house, so that she felt quite ready for an evening out. The dress wasn't exactly right, of course, but it was one of her nicest, a sleeveless green one with a low round neck and a swirl to the skirt, and just in case they should be dancing this evening she had popped her green sandals into the boot of the black two-seater.

At eight o'clock they were already on their way, and by half past they had reached the sprawling town on the other side of the mountains. Linda couldn't recognise the town as the one in which she had parted from Eve Bayes on her first day in Portugal; it seemed so different. Then, she had driven through in siesta hour, and it had looked terribly hot and somnolent. Now there were lights in every window, and gay awnings over the pavements outside the cafés. The open-air tables were crowded, chiefly with men as in Merida, though here and there an engaged couple sat with a duenna, or married people sat in a group, the women exchanging polite talk while their husbands gossiped more loudly.

There was a cinema emblazoned with neon, a huge poster depicting well-known Hollywood actors in an old dubbed film. There was a new theatre, a large hotel, more cafés, and in the centre of the main thoroughfare a discreet sign above a small but tasteful entrance, announcing the Estrella. Mike parked the car, Linda changed her shoes and gave her make-up a final check, and together they entered the rich little lobby and were in a world rather different from that of the crowded pavements and cinemas.

'A drink first,' Mike decided. 'Let's go into the lounge.'

They had a table in a corner which was almost completely screened from the rest of the room by feathery palm leaves. Mike ordered cocktails and Linda tapped her fingers to the muted rhythm of the gipsy band in the dining-room.

'I'm longing to dance!' Linda said.

'I'm not too good,' Mike answered cautiously, 'but I can have a go.' He lifted his glass. 'Here's to the first time. Let's hope there'll be many more.'

But the glass had not reached his lips when a steward bowed beside the table and spoke to him. He shrugged at Linda.

'This place is so exclusive that you sign a register when you come in. I forgot to do it, so I'll have to slide off for a second. Excuse me?'

She nodded and smiled, leaned back in the silk chair and sipped the cocktail. She could see very little but the potted palms and a pink crystal mirror in which her complexion was a wonderful bronze. She remembered the night before she had left England, the farewell party her father had arranged at the local hotel. That was the last time she had danced in a ball-room, but she had felt too queer inside to enjoy it much. She meant to enjoy every moment tonight, even if she wore poor Mike to shreds.

She half closed her eyes and listened to the fast, exciting music way off in the dining-room; became aware that it wasn't Mike back in his seat opposite her but ... but Luis. Her eyes opened fully, her fingers tightened on the small glass. 'The Senhor Marquez!' she said, with an attempt at lightness. 'It seems all roads from Merida lead to the Estrella tonight. I'm sure you didn't expect to see me here. How *did* you see me, by the way?'

He nodded sideways at the mirror. 'In a Portuguese club there is never any position which is entirely remote from the public gaze. This particular corner, by the way, is used almost exclusively by tourists. Never by Portuguese.'

His tone, very level and cool, steeled her. Perversely, she said, 'So for once I've instinctively done the right thing, or perhaps Mike knows this place rather better than he pretends. I imagine the food is delicious.'

Luis leaned forward with the sleeves of his dinner jacket along his knees and those long strong fingers loosely clasped. 'You have had a good day?'

'A wonderful day, and it's moving very pleasantly towards the climax. At least, I think it is.'

'You are not so sure now that I am here?'

Her heart moved, and settled. 'Do you disapprove of Jacinto's nurse coming to this place?'

'No. In other circumstances I might bring you here myself. Did you not enjoy the dancing in Merida?'

'It was exciting to watch, but it's been the sort of day that should definitely finish on a high note and we couldn't join in the dancing there.' She looked at him curiously, felt the throbbing in her throat which was part of being alone with him, anywhere. 'Did you see us in Merida?'

'Yes, I saw you. I also saw you slip away.'

She hesitated, looking at her fingers. 'Has Jacinto been all right today?'

'I believe so. Doña Velira has her daughter at the Palacio. Myself, I have been busy.'

'Then ... then you didn't see the flower procession this morning?'

'Yes, I saw it.' He paused, asked coolly, 'Did you go to the Gruta de Santa Maria?'

She nodded. 'It was unearthly. There was no one else about and we picnicked in the clearing.'

'And in the afternoon you drove again?'

'We took your advice and dozed.' Conscious of electricity

in the air, she added quickly, 'The siesta habit is a good one. I feel I could stay up all night!'

What he would have said then is problematical. Mike turned up, looked without much surprise at the Marquez and said droopily, 'Good evening, Luis. Linda, my pet, we're out of luck. I hadn't booked a table, and they're full, all the evening. I said we'd hang on for a bit on the chance of their having a cancellation, but frankly I don't think there's much hope.'

Luis was standing. 'Perhaps you two will give me the pleasure of dining with me? I came in here merely by chance this evening and am quite alone.'

'Then you can't have booked a table either,' said Mike.

'If you will excuse me I will see to it.'

They watched him go. Mike snapped his fingers morosely. 'Just like that,' he remarked. 'I am the Marquez de Filano, therefore the best table will swiftly be placed at my disposal.' He sighed. 'If he stays with us I'll get tight; I know it. Shall we escape while there's time?'

'We can't. Why should Luis be any different here from anywhere else?'

'He just is. Tonight I feel he hates my hide.'

'Don't be ridiculous. Why should he?'

'Because he's the great Luis and I'm in his way in one or two directions. Compared with him I'm a nonentity, but I happen to go over rather well with his girlfriend, and now I'm paying too much attention to a member of his staff that he doesn't want to lose.' He looked at her more closely. 'You've either a touch of the sun or a quickened heartbeat.'

She touched her warm cheek with the backs of her fingers. 'The cocktail,' she said quickly. 'Don't worry about the Marquez. He'll probably eat with us and then go.'

But an hour later, when coffee and coñac were served at the table on the edge of the circular dance floor, Luis offered cigarettes, clipped a cigar for himself and sat back to enjoy a pair of professional dancers who were spotlighted on the darkened floor.

Linda sat facing the table and the performers with Luis on her right and Mike to the left, and in the dim light of the small table lamp her face was so much in shadow that while following the motions of the dancers she could also watch the bold, angular profile which was half turned from her. She had never seen him look so austerely handsome; the sight of him twisted her heart.

During the meal Luis' manner had eased somewhat. Mike was not at his best, and it was possible that one or two of his fatuous remarks had reminded Luis that this young architect was not a dangerous personality but merely one who could at times be irritating. The Marquez had applauded a singer, been faintly amused by an acrobat and was now, apparently, fairly interested in the dancers who pirouetted and postured in a frenzy of rhythm; but he remained inscrutable.

The pair collapsed on the last music beat, took their applause as more lights glowed, and glided away. The band struck up for general dancing, and a few couples began to take to the gleaming floor.

'Shall we try it, Linda?' asked Mike.

'I'd love to.'

But the dance was not a success. Mike's description of his efforts as 'having a go' proved to be apt, and when he brought her back to the table Linda was relieved to sit down and rest the feet he had mistreated. Luis ordered more wine, pressed out the scarcely smoked cigar.

With distant courtesy he bent towards Linda. 'May I have the honour?'

She felt her throat tighten, and hesitated before saying, 'Please don't think you have to, senhor. These people know you . . .'

But he was already standing, and as she cast him a swift upward glance she saw a hard glitter in the dark eyes. He took her hand in a grip that bruised, his arm was rigid across her back, and he danced with mechanical perfection for quite two minutes before she felt him relax slightly. Oddly, it was she who spoke first.

'I made you angry again,' she said.

'It is something I begin to expect—this way you have of speaking sometimes without first thinking,' he answered. 'You dance well.'

'Thank you.'

'But there are too many people here now. Let us go outside.'

The french doors opened on to a terrace at the back of the building, and below the stone balustrade lay a small enclosed garden which smelled of lemon-flowers and carnations. They moved to the ornamental stone wall and stood there, looking out at a dark sky radiant with stars. The music in the room behind them came to an end and the lights again went low. A

131

pianist played the opening bars of 'Clair de Lune' and a violin joined in; two more performers, apparently.

He looked down at the narrow shoulder-piece of her dress, the slim bare arms. 'You are warm enough?' he asked.

'Yes. The air's like wine. That's a trite saying, but it's true of Portugal. It's strange to think that the mountains are between us and Merida; makes you feel you're a long way from home, though it's only twenty miles or so.'

'You think of Merida as home?'

'Wherever one lives is home, isn't it? I've even thought of a hotel as home when I've been on holiday.'

'By that I am to take it that you regard the Palacio as you would regard a hotel?'

'No, of course not, senhor, but it's rather difficult for anyone in my position to get a permanent feeling for such a place. That's natural, isn't it?'

'Possibly. So much depends on the kind of person you are.' He stopped and looked down at her again with an unreadable expression. 'I have never yet been able to discover exactly what you are thinking.'

Linda said slowly, 'I could say the same of you, except that I've no right to. But I do realise it's difficult for you to be spontaneous.'

'You feel I am never spontaneous?'

'Well . . . I don't expect it. I know that I've been too much the other way, but by your standards I believe I'm improving. Everything you do has to be according to plan.'

'Go on,' he said quietly.

'I'd rather not, senhor.'

'There is no one to hear, and in my opinion this discussion is overdue. You resent the way I live, my attitude towards others, the fact that there are certain rules which I rigidly enforce. These rules, by the way, have always been part of my position at Merida. What else do you resent?'

'There's no resentment,' she said, 'none at all. I think it's just lack of understanding. I mean my understanding of you and your kind, though I'm trying to learn. I don't suppose you're able to do anything without being guided by some code, or some special knowledge.'

A smile sounded in his voice. '*Any*thing, pequena? The ordering of a puppy, for instance, or the blind eye to the hidden thermometer? That kind of thing?'

'They weren't spur-of-the-moment, were they?' she said

apologetically. 'Being the iron hand over a vast household has probably made you forget what it's like to experience an impulse. You did ask me to be frank, senhor.'

His tone was tantalizing. 'You think I never know an impulse? But you are wrong! I have never known so many impulses as during these last few weeks; if I had indulged them I would be branded irresponsible and possibly worse!'

'Really?' She turned to him, wide-eyed. 'You suppressed them and no one knew? I wonder what they were?'

'What is it that impels any man to sudden anger, sudden happiness, the need for sudden speed on the road? It is generally the striking of a spark, and sparks should be watched carefully or they swiftly cause flames.' His voice mocked. 'Supposing one saw a mouth that was sweet as flowers and felt a compulsion to kiss it. Here in Portugal, a kiss can change one's world.'

She said a little shakily, 'It can do that anywhere, senhor.'

He asked casually, 'Has your world changed since you met Michael Cullum?'

She managed a laugh. 'He hasn't kissed me, if that's what you mean . . . not quite, anyway.'

Luis' drawn breath was audible. 'What does that imply— not quite?'

'He's unhappy sometimes. Mike's not the simple type he appears. In his private life he's not very successful.'

'Yet he seems to do very well,' he said abruptly. 'I know that he is often at the house of Senhor del Carros, and we see him at the Palacio at least once a week. Doña Velira is now insisting that you need the kind of companionship that Cullum can give.'

It was like being jolted into a river, the cold straight stream of Doña Velira and her plans. Linda took her lip between her teeth and looked once more at the black outlines of the trees against the star-studded sky. They must have been out here for some time; 'Clair de Lune' had ended, and a man was singing in one of those liquid trembling voices which are calculated to pluck at the heartstrings of even the cynic. He sang about the delights of amor and luar, and because it was in Portuguese it sounded much more thrilling than the well-worn love and moonlight.

'We ought to go in,' she said dully.

'We cannot do so till the song is finished.' He paused, and added evenly. 'You understand what he sings?'

133

'It sounds like the usual sentimental chorus,' she replied. 'One has to be in the mood to be moved by it.'

'You are too young to speak like that,' he said curtly. 'There is something about you these days which makes one think you have had an unhappy love affair. It was not noticeable when you first came to Merida, yet I know that nothing of this sort has happened to you since you have been with us. If it were Cullum, you could have him easily—I am sure of that.'

Linda squared her shoulders. 'Nothing so devastating as a love muddle,' she said with her politest smile. 'I've had a long day. Don't you think we ought to go in to Mike?'

Thinking only that this was the imperative point at which to end the talk with him, she moved towards the door while the singer was still quivering aloud with love. Luis caught her arm to restrain her and held her there in front of him. She felt him behind her, tall and strong and painfully near, leaned back a fraction in spite of herself and felt his other hand grasp her shoulder and press her against him. For crazy seconds she closed her eyes and felt his breath in her hair, the unconscious movement of his thumb over the fine bones of her shoulder. She couldn't breathe.

The hand-clapping broke in like an alarum. She swayed a little as he released her, walked forward blindly into the glare of lights. Sick and frightened with the intensity of her own emotions, she went straight to the table where Mike was clasping an almost empty wine bottle. Luis was at her side, persuading Mike back into his seat.

He spoke calmly. 'We left you too long alone with the wine, my friend. You cannot drive tonight. I will take Miss Grey back to the Palacio, and as we leave I will ask someone to telephone your sister. It would be wiser for you to stay with her tonight.'

'Nonsense,' said Mike with surprising belligerence. 'I could drive that bus anywhere.'

'But not across the mountains,' Luis told him decisively. 'In any case, now that you are here, why not stay in Portão for a day or two? You will excuse us?'

Mike said, 'What's happened to Linda? She was red and now she's white.'

'Goodnight, my friend,' said Luis firmly. 'I will certainly see that your sister is telephoned at once. No doubt your brother-in-law will arrive very soon.'

Linda felt that compelling hand once more on her arm. In the foyer Luis made his request on Mike's behalf, and then he took her out into the street, where an occasional neon light illumined the cobbled roadway.

Her throat harsh, she said, 'My things are in Mike's car. May I get them?'

He took her along to the two-seater, found her walking shoes and the plant, and carried them to his own car. He saw her seated and slid behind the wheel. Linda put her bag on the seat between them and wished she could light a cigarette to steady her pulsing nerves. Her clenched fists had tightened till her fingernails cut into her palms, but now, by degrees, her tension was easing and she was sliding into a fatalistic frame of mind.

Luis drove without speaking. They left Portão, climbed right away from the town into the blackness of low mountains. The granite road curved and dipped, so that at one minute the car beams picked out crags and hill pastures, and at the next there were only the stars ahead as if they were driving into eternity.

Presently, as was inevitable, Linda was back on the terrace of the Estrella. She dared not look at Luis, but she knew there was nothing in his demeanour to show that he had shared even the smallest emotional experience with Linda Grey. One of those impulses they had discussed? she wondered bitterly. A woman close in the darkness, someone young and foolish enough to tremble a little at his touch, so that vaguely he was stirred? Just as likely that it had been deliberate—to show her he was human in his reactions. He was hateful.

They were through the mountains and less than ten miles from Merida when he said, 'You must be tired now. Tomorrow you must have a quiet day and we will find time to go into a plan I have for you and Jacinto.'

She felt like telling him not to bother about plans—she would be moving out. But she was too weary, and answered, 'Very well, senhor,' and continued to look out of the window.

It was the only break in the silence of that journey. There were few lights in the Palacio as they went up the drive, but the usual glow from above the big main door lit up the fountain. He pulled up and came round to her, made no comment when she avoided his touch, but leaned into the car to gather up the plant and the pair of shoes. He looked more closely at the silver-green leaves and discovered it was a pot of basil. He

135

closed the car door, and in that moment the plant and pot lay shattered on the tiles.

'Careless of me,' he said. 'We must get you another.'

'That's all right,' she answered very coolly. 'If I can't do without one I'll get Mike to replace it for me. Thank you for the drive.'

She almost snatched the shoes from him and hurried into the hall. But at the foot of the stairs he caught up with her.

'Your purse!' he said.

It was an envelope-shaped bag and she caught too swiftly at the flap. The fastening sprang open, the contents spilled; compact, a few coins, lipstick and a nail file clattered about her feet. Luis bent and scooped them up, gave them to her. Gave her all of them except a small oval medallion of St Francis. It lay in his stretched palm while he stared at her with eyes as black and hard as jet. Her lips went dry and stiff. She swept the medallion from his hand and into her bag, turned and fled up the staircase.

CHAPTER NINE

JACINTO was delighted to have Linda back again. He told her so next morning. He took her out to show her the puppies as if she had been away for weeks, and he even told her their names were Niki and Fransi in case she had forgotten. Later, during their walk, he climbed his small tree so cleverly that he begged to be allowed to show off for Papa. But Linda's heart turned whenever she thought of the Marquez. She was unutterably relieved when Doña Velira told her at lunch-time that Luis had been called away on business and would not return to the Palacio till the weekend.

'It seems he has some plans for the summer villa—possibly you and Jacinto are to go there with servants—Quite certainly I must stay here to keep matters correct for Nolette's visits to the Palacio, but it is natural, of course, that he should want Jacinto to be elsewhere.' She paused, and the hooded lids flickered down, once. 'Have you discovered how long Mr Cullum is staying here?'

'He's uncertain, but I'm sure you needn't worry about him and Senhorita del Carros.'

Doña Velira smiled like a satisfied eagle. 'I am very pleased with you, Miss Grey. It was a good move for you to spend the whole day with him yesterday. I invited Nolette for lunch and she stayed with us for tea. It was only because her father had invited some of his oldest friends from a distant wine farm to meet her that she returned home for dinner. For the first time I was able to leave Luis and Nolette here alone together yesterday afternoon.'

Linda heard herself saying, 'You didn't feel that Senhorita del Carros needed a duenna?'

The old lady gave her experienced smile. 'They are not children, and it is natural that they should not wish me to hear all they have to say to each other.' She sighed. 'Rico is only five years younger than Luis, but I would not feel happy about his being alone with the girl he loves. He is a good boy but not enough serious. I am getting impatient with him.'

'Have you heard from him at all, senhora?'

The ornamental hair combs gleamed dully as she shook her head. 'It is nothing, I suppose. From Brazil, he did not write more often than once a month, and sometimes he would wait so long that Luis would cable him, commanding him to write to me at once. Such a beautiful letter he would send then, full of amazement at the time which had passed since he had last written. The dear one forgets, and when he is reminded he cannot be humble enough.'

Which was typically Rico. 'He's not so far away now,' Linda said conventionally.

'No, but I doubt very much that he has stayed all this time in Portão. He has been persuaded to go on to Lisbon or Oporto. The wicked boy,' she ended lovingly.

Linda did not wonder about Rico for long. His scheme, she thought, had had all the hallmarks of a flop, and she imagined that he was now torn between the ridiculous pride which kept him idle because he was a de Filano, and the desire to fly, even if he had to take a job with an airline. She rather thought that in time the airline would win, and she hoped she wouldn't be around when Doña Velira learned about it!

The day was singularly quiet, and so was the following day, until the evening, when Nolette and Mike Cullum arrived together. It was about six o'clock, and Linda was supervising Jacinto's supper in the nursery, when Nolette came in and asked the little boy, very charmingly, if she might sit with him till he was ready for bed. She nodded to Linda and sank down into the easy chair.

Smiling at Jacinto, she said, 'I have good news for you, meu caro. At the end of next week we take you to the sea. You will like that?'

'Linda will come?' he asked. 'I will only like it if Linda comes.'

'But naturally. A little boy always travels with his nurse. You are to stay there with Miss Grey for perhaps six weeks, and possibly when you come back there will be changes here at the Palacio.'

Jacinto couldn't envisage changes at the Palacio; he didn't even try. 'I shall like the sea with Linda,' he said.

'You remember the villa at San Domingo?'

He thought. 'No, but I remember the sea. It was a long time ago.'

'Tia Velira tells me you were a baby of two years, so that is a very good memory, Jacinto. Drink your milk, my child; it is good for you.'

Linda said, 'Don't hurry him, please. He'll drink it.'

Nolette leaned back, said with sharp-eyed pleasantness, 'Have you noticed, Miss Grey, that Jacinto is more lively and talkative since I have been modelling him? I have drawn him out a little, I think.'

'Perhaps, but the puppies deserve some of the credit. He can talk to them without fear of being thought impolite.'

Just faintly, Nolette hardened. 'You like to dominate in your own sphere, no? I know that is true of English nurses, but it is time you learned that one does not tolerate high-handedness from the staff in Portuguese families. Your position is above that of the servants, but you must not feel that because the Marquez is good enough to permit you certain privileges you can say what you please to anyone. Remember,' she added slowly and with a nice degree of emphasis, 'that those privileges will no doubt cease when the Marquez marries.'

'I'm quite aware of that.' Linda looked pointedly at Jacinto. 'I'd rather we didn't discuss this now, if you don't mind.'

'The child cannot understand,' said Nolette, the firmness of contempt in her voice. She appraised Linda's plain blue dress with white at the neck and cuffs, the corn-coloured hair which curled naturally back from her forehead. 'I suppose in England you are considered pretty?'

'Passably—nothing shattering.'

'Yet you are twenty-two and have no fiancé. Is that usual?'

'It happens,' said Linda briefly.

'But I will be charitable and say that a girl with your looks, even though they are not vivid, could marry if she wished. Why do you not wish, Miss Grey? Did you have ambitions?'

'I didn't happen to fall in love.'

Nolette's exquisitely curved mouth took on a sarcastic slant. 'I believe I understand. That little knowledge of Portuguese which you possessed opened a new world to you. There was the opportunity of this post at the Palacio, the chance of meeting and marrying a member of a good family. Perhaps someone had told you that our dark men are fascinated by fair women. And now you find it is not true. I am sorry for you, Miss Grey.'

'You needn't be. After all, there's still time, isn't there?'

'I do not care for that tone!'

Very coolly, Linda said, 'Then don't annoy me into using it. And will you please stop talking like this with the child here?

He's unlikely to understand what you're saying, but any child is sensitive to sharp tones, and it's almost his bedtime.'

Nolette stood up, lifted her head arrogantly. 'This is appalling insolence, Miss Grey! I can only assume that you have been disappointed here, and cannot bear the subject of your hopes and desires.'

Linda crossed to open the door. 'I don't care what you assume. My only anxiety is that you should do it elsewhere.'

Nolette hesitated, walked to the door. 'Come with me!'

For a moment Linda was tempted to ignore the summons. Then she looked back at Jacinto, saw that he was interested but not upset. She smiled at him, lifted a finger to show she would not be long, and went out into the corridor with the other woman.

Nolette was taller, her dark head was thrown back so that the thin, aristocratic nostrils showed very clearly. Her manner had changed, indefinably.

'You spoke in heat because of the little one,' she said, 'so I will not demand an apology. But it is as well for you to know that I have heard much about you—from Doña Velira, Mr Cullum, and from the Marquez himself. With your impossible demands on behalf of Jacinto you have made yourself far too important. You have entered spheres which are outside your duties, and I should not be surprised to learn that it is through you that Enrico de Filano cannot face betrothal to Juanita Montales. But do not think that Rico will marry you! He is too obedient a son for that.'

'Why bring Rico into this?'

'Because Rico's wife will have to be received here at the Palacio. You are not dense, Miss Grey. I am sure you understand!'

Yes, Linda understood. The picture of Nolette as the Marqueza receiving Linda de Filano, wife of Rico, might have been funny had it not been heart-searing. She contrived a pale smile.

'I've no designs on Rico. What made you think I might have?'

'Mr Cullum told me that Rico professed to love you.'

'He loves me about as much as Mike does. In different ways they're both frustrated and I've listened to their troubles.'

Nolette's dark glance became fixed. 'Michael Cullum has troubles? What are they?'

'Ask him. I must go back to Jacinto.'

140

'But wait,' said Nolette peremptorily. 'Is it possible that in your conceit you have also mistaken Mr Cullum's kindness to you? Did you not know that more than a week ago he asked me to show him the flower procession? I could not do it because I had already promised to come here on the day of the festa for lunch with Luis!'

It was only in that moment that Linda realised the extent of the other's regal vanity. She was all set to marry Luis and to keep what she probably termed 'undesirable elements' out of the de Filano family. Yet Mike, being a successful architect and of different race and therefore in her opinion worth cultivating as an admirer, had become part of her world in Merida; so much so that she could not contemplate his interest in any other woman. Nolette del Carros had not been using Mike to inflame Luis, or only desultorily; she really believed that her beauty and the power in her fingertips had enslaved him. She was probably very meticulous about leaving Mike in no doubt as to her own lack of feeling for him, but she was nevertheless willing to bask in his complete subjection to her beauty and her art.

Linda said, 'Don't worry, senhora. I'm not interested in Mike, either. Thanks for the talk. It's been enlightening.' And she went back into the nursery.

Watching Jacinto undress and playing with him in and out of the bathroom helped her limbs to cease their quivering, and by the time she had him in bed and was giving him an instalment of the usual unending bedtime story, she could look back with a degree of detachment to those minutes with Nolette. She kissed Jacinto, promised she would later say goodnight to Niki and Fransi, and set the communicating door to her own room at its usual angle.

Because he would have heard her in the bedroom, she went back to the nursery. The table had been cleared and the jar of roses replaced at its centre, the chair had been set back against the wall. The tidiness irked her, and she opened the french door and went out to the balcony, where the wrought-iron grille had been heightened for safety by the addition of curlecues. She looked between the twisted bars at the early darkness and she saw, below, the big wired enclosure with a kennel at one end and the two puppies blandly asleep in a small dark mass on the grass. She tried to think of life with Jacinto and the dogs at some palatial villa on the coast, but somehow she knew it would never happen. Or if the holiday began, it would end quickly.

Now it had become apparent that sending Jacinto and his nurse to the summer villa had been Nolette's idea. They had talked it over during her absence with Mike the other day, and possibly it had been Luis' first step towards a proposal. He would do everything correctly, even to having the Palacio free from the child who was not Nolette's. Jacinto would be safe with Miss Grey and could be forgotten while the discreet festivities of the betrothal took place. And Linda was sure that if Nolette had her way the villa at the coast would become Jacinto's permanent residence.

Linda remained there in the balcony with her depression for some time. A servant came and told her in scandalised tones that Doña Velira wished her to come at once for dinner.

Linda was unmoved. 'Please tell the senhora that I'm very sorry but I can't come down this evening.'

'There are visitors,' he urged her. 'Senhorita del Carros and Senhor Cullum.'

'Yes, I know. Please ask them to excuse me.'

He looked flurried. 'May I say you have a headache?'

'Yes, if you like. It's half true, anyway.'

'Very well. I will send you a tray.'

'Just coffee and a sandwich,' she said. 'Thank you.'

The tray came, piled with fruit and salad, and with the requested sandwiches on a silver plate. She fingered the flowered edge of the plate and thought of the table downstairs, the sparkling glassware and huge gold dish-pedestal which always stood just above Luis' place so that he could serve the meats; only he wasn't there tonight.

But there would come night after night when he would be there, with Nolette in the place now occupied by Doña Velira. Doña Velira would be given a house of her own somewhere in the vicinity, and a new family would grow up here in the Palacio Filano. There would be balls, house guests, artistic dilettante types from Paris and Madrid as well as the Portuguese nobility, and perhaps Mike would receive an occasional command to spend a weekend under the splendid steeples of the Palacio.

She got through three cups of coffee. At about nine-thirty she went down to give the puppies warm milk and place them in the kennel. She fastened the small door so that they had air but could not get out, patted each sleepy head and crawled out of the enclosure into the warm summer darkness.

142

She recalled the darkness on the terrace of the Estrella in Portão, and she thought how terrible a trick of the imagination could be. Luis had stopped her from disturbing a singer, that was all. Her absurd pulses had done the rest! It was that moment which had exaggerated the incidents of the pot of basil and Rico's medallion. They were negligible, really; the whole evening had been negligible. The sooner she accepted it, the better.

Doña Velira, it seemed, was not one to lose the advantage in any game if she could help it. She came to the nursery at midmorning, smiling in her suspect manner and greeting both Linda and the child with condescending benevolence. She remained standing, a slight, well-knit figure in black silk and pearls, her hair faultlessly piled and secured with a plain black comb. In spite of the elegance she looked old and wily, and instinctively Linda prepared herself for whatever might come.

'So we have Saturday again,' said the foreign voice, as the bony beringed fingers hooked themselves playfully into Jacinto's hair. 'You will be free at noon, Miss Grey. Do you have plans?'

'I've things to do—shampooing my hair and some sewing. I was out all day Wednesday, so I don't mind staying in today.'

'But it is not necessary. I have a friend who will bring her small granddaughter—she is about six. The companionship you are always urging for the boy, eh?' She looked grotesquely roguish, which should have been a warning. 'You must go out, Miss Grey. My nephew would insist on it. As a matter of fact, I arranged it with Mr Cullum while he was here last night. For your own good, you understand?'

It was disgracefully obvious, and Linda was almost past caring how she spoke to anyone. 'You're working it to death, senhora, and for no reason. Whatever you were after has been accomplished.'

'Perhaps, but one cannot let it rest there. I believe you will be leaving here with the boy next weekend. I want you to persuade Mr Cullum to leave also, for England.'

'I can't possibly do that. Why should he break off his holiday simply because I ask it?'

In a tone of reproof, Doña Velira answered, 'You are addressing the Senhora de Filano. I am afraid Nolette is right; you go beyond yourself occasionally.'

'It's not part of my job to keep Michael Cullum occupied,'

returned Linda. 'If you don't like his friendliness with Nolette, tell him so.'

'But that would be to expose everything we are thinking and planning. Nolette does not realise how much this friendship she has for the Englishman is against Luis' feelings, and though I have hinted I am not heeded. It is asking very little of you, Miss Grey. You still like this Mr Cullum?'

'He's all right. It's the intrigue I don't care for.'

'There is no intrigue,' said Doña Velira soothingly. 'Mr Cullum has said he would be charmed to take you for a drive this afternoon, and to dinner with his sister at the house this evening. I was clever enough to make it appear that he had suggested it, not I. It is possible that Luis will return some time today, and his first thought will, of course, be to see Nolette. The del Carros quinta is too close to the villa of Mrs Bayes, and I am afraid Senhor del Carros has made Mr Cullum too welcome. He calls there whenever he has nothing else to do.' She softened insidiously. 'So you will see that he drives you far this afternoon, my child, and if you cannot put into his head this idea that he must return to England, you may suggest that his attentions to Nolette might be unpleasing to the Marquez.' More energetically she went on, 'I am quite certain he is the reason the betrothal has been delayed, but the arrangements which are now being made for you to take Jacinto to the sea show clearly how Luis is thinking. I want no hurt for him in this matter. As I have told you before, his happiness is very dear to me.'

It was the last sentence which silenced any further protest from Linda. She said, 'Yes, I know it is. I think you'd better give me permission to be quite frank with Mr Cullum.'

'But not to use my name, Miss Grey!'

'Very well. Is he coming at two?'

The older woman nodded, and said graciously, 'You may lunch up here with Jacinto, if you wish. I will send Lupe to rouse the child at three-thirty.' And she sailed out like a slim, aged yacht on becalmed waters.

As it happened, Linda did not get much conversation with Mike that afternoon. He called and picked her up, apologised ruefully for getting a bit 'high' at the Estrella, and then talked moodily of some business correspondence he had received from England this morning. He was putting in a design for a factory up north and another for a block of flats in a London suburb, but he wished he could get a stab at something truly

144

artistic; most of all he would have liked to let himself go on a modern museum building.

Linda did not listen very closely. She saw the carpets of flowers in the sun-drenched valley, the low, undulating hills, the vineyards and cottages, and again a part of the valley with the river winding its lazy course between olives and osiers, wild mimosas and lemon trees. He took a short steep road that she did not know, drove out on to a promontory and stopped in a spot that looked like the edge of the world.

For some time they sat there in silence, Mike staring over the valley and the hills, the soft shapes of the mountains beyond the hidden town of Merida. Linda was entranced, looking in all directions for landmarks. She pointed back at the road lower down, shaded her eyes as she gazed into the distance.

'That must be the Palacio, right over there,' she said. 'Those vast lawns look as big as handkerchiefs, don't they? If we had binoculars we might see the steeples above the trees!'

Mike transferred his stare, and became absorbed. 'That can't be a bird flapping around over the Palacio,' he said. 'We couldn't see anything that size from here. It's a plane.'

Linda watched . . . and froze. 'Mike,' she whispered. 'It must be Rico. He's done it.'

'Done what?'

'Brought someone's aircraft from Lisbon. Oh, heavens! What do we do?'

'Is it our concern?' he asked. 'Stop looking as if you've seen a zombie and tell me that it's all about.'

With wide eyes she went on watching the small silver and black thing which banked and dipped, climbed steeply and came round to repeat the performance.

'The idiot! Surely he realises that these antics will only convince everyone that he's not fit to have charge of a plane!' She looked entreatingly at Mike, saw his exasperation and said, 'He didn't go to friends in Portão. He went to Lisbon because some man who owns a plane was supposed to be willing to go halves or something in this air service scheme. He had some idea of bringing that flying friend of his and four passengers—and some freight—here to Merida. He's been gone so long that I decided it had all fallen through. But . . . but here he is!'

'If he has passengers up there,' commented Mike, 'and he ever gets them down to earth again, they'll be sueing him in the courts. What's the matter with the chap—delirious?'

'The plane probably goes like a bird, and he's demonstrating to Luis and his mother what a tricky pilot he is. Only Luis is away and his mother will think it's someone else gone mad.' She swung round suddenly. 'Mike, don't just sit there! Take me back.'

'To the Palacio?' he said dazedly. 'You don't suppose he intends landing on one of the lawns?'

'No, I believe he had a field picked out. But I ought to warn the senhora, because Luis isn't there to do it. I feel dreadful about this!'

'But why should you? The chap's definitely crazy.'

'Well . . . well, I knew about it, and no one else did. If he'd simply landed somewhere and turned up looking breezy and confident it would have been all right. But with Rico almost turning somersaults up there, there's sure to be trouble, and they'll have to know I was in on this trip.'

'You mean he'll drag you into it? He's not such a rat!'

'It isn't that. It's just that I have to warn the senhora.'

'You're too darned conscientious, my pet. Let him land and make his presence known in his own way. We'll keep out of it all day, and even if they find out that you were in on his plans, by tomorrow it won't seem so important.'

There seemed to be sense in this advice. Linda twisted her fingers together and watched the small plane level out; it was moving away from the Palacio at last and would probably circle towards its destination. This demonstration over the Palacio was something she would never have envisaged, and she could only conclude that the success of this initial venture had gone to Rico's head. In about an hour he would present himself to his mother and demand to see Luis, confident of victory. Perhaps, as Luis was not there, he still stood a chance; he might have the sense to play down his mother's horror at his accomplishment. But he deserved whatever he got for his stupidity.

Mike started up the car. 'Let's get out of the valley,' he said. 'We'll pretend it wasn't Rico at all. It needn't have been, you know.'

'Don't go yet!'

Linda was leaning forward, straining to see the plane as it came lower. She swung out of the car and went forward to the edge of the promontory, and the next second Mike was beside her, pulling her back to safety. Together, they saw the plane swoop down till it seemed only a few yards above the tree-

146

tops, glimmering silver as it banked a little too steeply. The wing-tip caught the trees down there in the valley, the plane shuddered violently and met the pasture with force, curveted and came to rest.

Her face dead white, Linda said, 'Will it catch fire?'

'No reason why it should,' Mike answered, a little shakily. 'Look here, we can't wait here to see if they fight their way out. I'll drive back to Merida and tell the police and get what other help and transport I can. I'll drop you at the Palacio on the way.'

'Can't we go straight down to the plane?'

'Cottagers will have seen it and they'll go down. We can't do a thing on our own.'

He had the car moving when she said, 'Well, I'll have to tell Doña Velira now—or get someone to do it. Mike . . . do you suppose they're all safe?'

'Of course. It wasn't really much of a bump, and they would have been strapped in their seats before the aerobatics. The wing-tip looked damaged and the wheels must have buckled, but that's about all. Stop worrying, Linda. Anyone would think you had a crush on Rico.'

'You don't understand. Step on it, Mike.'

He obeyed, and in less than fifteen minutes he had stopped, at Linda's request, near the Palacio gates. She slipped out, waved perfunctorily as he moved off again, and turned to run up the drive. Even in the moment of stress she remembered that this was no way for an adult to approach the Palacio, but she did not ease up. She hastened into the terrace, entered the small sala and found it empty. She went through to the hall and bounded up the stairs, and at the top she remembered that Lupe was supposed to be getting Jacinto up at about this time; so she turned right.

Lupe, with a towel over her arm, was just closing the nursery door. She stood still, apparently bracing herself to comprehend the English with which Miss Grey would address her. But Linda did her best in Portuguese.

'Lupe, did you see the plane overhead just now?'

The thin mouth wrinkled with ire. 'Everyone saw it,' she said. 'The senhora is going to complain to the authorities. She was terrified.'

'You'll have to tell her, Lupe . . . Rico was in that plane.'

The woman gave a muted shriek. 'Dom Enrico? I cannot believe it. The senhora will certainly make a big complaint!

147

How dare they fly the planes so, with Doña Velira's son as a passenger? I must tell the senhora!'

She was half-way up the corridor when Linda called, 'Do it gently, Lupe. And tell her the plane has landed in the valley.'

Linda pressed a hand to the painful knocking above her left eye. She leaned back against the wall and willed the sick sensation from her head and throat. Should she have said more to Lupe? Was it better for Doña Velira to learn by halves? How she wished Luis were here; even his anger would be bearable so long as one knew he was in charge. The smallest catastrophe in his absence sent everyone to pieces, and this was in the nature of a disaster.

Those people in the plane—how could one be sure they were all unharmed? Would Mike let her know? Or would it be possible to order the car and go down to the scene herself?

Jacinto came out of his room and smiled at her with heart-warming delight. 'You are back, Linda! You will stay with me now?'

'Are you alone, darling?' she asked mechanically.

'There was Lupe, but she has gone.' He took her hand, said cajolingly, 'Stay and play with the puppies. When I am big I will have thousands of dogs!'

She was cut off up here and it made her frantic. She said, 'Wait in the nursery. I'll get you a cool drink.'

Plainly this was beyond Jacinto; when one wanted a cool drink one pressed the bell. But he obediently went into the nursery, and Linda ran along the corridor and down the stairs. And there in the hall she met a beady-eyed old lady and a small girl with black ringlets. Lupe came from somewhere, scurrying and curtseying, and there were some excited exchanges in Portuguese.

Then Lupe turned to Linda. 'Please, Miss Grey, the senhora is prostrate and asks that you take care of the senhorito and this little menina for a while. She thinks it would be best if you took them for a long walk in the gardens.'

'Has she acted in any way about the plane?' Linda asked quickly.

'She has sent the car with the driver and a servant. Fortunately,' she smiled and curtseying again rather wildly in the direction of the old lady, 'we have one of the senhora's friends here. Miss Grey, you do not know what a relief it is that you were good enough to come back this afternoon, but the senhora cannot understand how you would know that her son is in the plane.'

Linda said, 'It doesn't matter at the moment,' and for the life of her she could say no more.

She went upstairs, met Jacinto's questioning stare and realised that she had come back without the drink but trailing a little black-eyed girl in stiff white silk with a pink sash.

The next few hours were nightmarish. Linda made chocolate for the children and took them out the back way into the grounds. The little girl was unyielding and quiet, and she was too frightened of the puppies to go into the enclosure with them. Niki and Fransi came out and gambolled; one of them bit a hole in Jacinto's sock, and the little girl went rigid when the other puppy made advances to her. So the frolicsome creatures had to be returned to their pen, and Linda set out with the children along the path to the orchard.

Neither child was accustomed to young company, and consequently they ignored each other. Linda tried to include both in various games, but only Jacinto understood her Portuguese; the little girl didn't even try to understand. Had Linda felt there was some chance that these two could become daily playmates she would have taken pains to find the right approach to the small stranger; as things were, she could only attempt a pleasant afternoon for them. Herself, she was painfully keyed up.

Soon after five she took the children back to the Palacio, and the little girl was immediately whisked off by a servant to a waiting car. Upstairs, there was mild activity among the maids, but Linda was unable to corner one of them. Jacinto went with her into her bedroom, and there she found a note from Mike, written on a page torn from his diary and slipped into one of the familiar crested envelopes. 'Everything under control, no lives lost. Bear up, honey, you can't get worse than the sack.'

The words put her back into fatalistic mood, and her nerves settled somewhat. In a way, the isolation up here was a protection; she mustn't think about what was happening over there in the other wing.

Jacinto played with his gliders, set up dominoes like a line of soldiers and sent the lot down with a smart click. He lay on the floor with a picture book in a way which had never been permitted before Linda had come to Merida, and read out

149

many of the words he remembered.

At ten minutes to six a maid brought his supper. On the point of asking for news, Linda found herself silent. It was only after the table had been set and the dishes placed that she inquired evenly,

'Has Doña Velira recovered from the shock of this afternoon?'

The maid, a young one who was a little shy of the English nurse, said softly, 'The senhora is better, Miss Grey, but the doctor has ordered her to rest in bed for a few days.'

'And Dom Enrico?'

'I do not know, senhora. We have prepared his room but he has not arrived.'

The maid escaped. Jacinto ate his supper and decided that for his exercise tonight he would use the skipping rope; as this was in the nature of a hopping walk round the room Linda did not object. She went through the usual bedtime routine with him, decided that as soon as she could be sure he was asleep she would have a bath.

She tidied the nursery, mended the torn sock even though she knew Jacinto would never wear it again. For something to do, she parcelled together a couple of small suits, some underwear, socks and shoes, all of them in excellent condition but marked in some way which made them unwearable for Jacinto; they would go to one of the poorer families in Merida.

Her watch said ten minutes past eight when Luis came in. She looked at it automatically, perhaps to evade the keen stare as he greeted her.

She answered him, added rather hurriedly, 'I didn't know you were back, senhor. I've been cut off up here for hours.'

'I returned half an hour ago,' he said sternly, 'and learned that what I had been striving for two days to prevent had happened.' He paused. 'It is not surprising that you are pale. How could you allow this thing?'

'Senhor . . .'

He waved a hand abruptly. 'This is not the time for argument. Come with me now. Rico is asking for you.'

Linda's fingers closed over the medallion she had kept in her pocket since the night it had spilled from her bag. 'Rico?' she echoed. 'Where is he?'

'He is in bed, in his room, and says he will not rest till he sees you.'

'Was he . . . hurt?'

'A dislocated shoulder and some bruises. He was attended to in the town and brought home this evening.' There was a metallic note in his voice which unpleasantly overlaid the sarcasm. 'He cannot rest without seeing you, but do not prepare yourself for a declaration; he is subdued and hardly in a condition to make love. Come!'

She moved a little jerkily, found herself in the corridor and walking with him. For the first time she passed right into the other wing, and Luis stopped to rap on a door and open it for her. Hesitantly she preceded him into the room.

She saw Rico propped up against pillows, his shoulder encased in white. There were bruises across his brow and one on the cheekbone, but his smile was a weak edition of the usual one, crooked and flashing. It was not until the figure rose from the seat beside the bed that she recognised Juanita. And across the room in a tapestry chair sat the indomitable duenna, Senhora Montales. Linda looked swiftly at Luis, saw an almost malicious mockery in his expression, and like lightning it came to her what she must do. Heaven help her if she bungled it.

She walked to the other side of the bed, opposite Juanita, looked down at Rico. 'You're lucky to be here like this,' she said. 'How do you feel?'

'Very sick,' he said pathetically. 'I am a big fool, no?'

'A very big fool, and you frightened your mother half to death.'

'It is too bad. I meant to dip only once over the Palacio, but it seemed such a small gesture after I had accomplished so much.' His voice lowered. 'I brought all those things, you know?'

Did he mean the jewels? She daren't look at Luis again. 'Did you? Even so, I'm afraid it was a failure.'

'And there will be compensation to pay,' he said with a sigh. Then he flashed her a look that pleaded with her to read his mind, and lifted his hand. 'I am afraid they are going to be vexed with you, and that is why I ask to see you. You forgive me for entangling you in this, Linda?'

Her heart beating high in her throat, she took her hand from her pocket and clasped his. He smiled suddenly, boyishly, then let his hand fall. Sweat stood out on Linda's temples as she moved back towards the foot of the bed.

Rico was saying, 'You must not mind this, Juanita. You

151

would not have understood or I would have told you instead of Miss Grey. But there was one thing I omitted. You know that, do you not?'

Juanita hid her embarrassment by turning her head. 'I think I know, Rico.'

'Will you please bring my white jacket from the wardrobe?'

Hands clenched clammily, steeled every second for Luis' intervention, Linda watched the dark girl reach down the jacket and bring it to Rico. She saw his hand go well down into an inside pocket, the oval of gold in his fingers, heard him say, thrillingly,

'I should have left this with you, Juanita, and then perhaps I would not have been tempted to risk my life. Take it now, and keep it for me till I am well.'

Overcome, Juanita bowed her head over the medallion he had placed in her palm. Linda caught Rico's glance, his shrug of humorous resignation to Juanita and the famous glass goblet factory of her father, and she was almost overwhelmed herself.

With rigid politeness Luis said, 'Enough excitement for one day, eh, Rico? You had better say goodnight to the senhora and Juanita. Come, Miss Grey!'

They were outside with the door closed. Luis gripped her arm and indicated the staircase, said in a raging undertone, 'Charming! Perfectly charming! Let us discuss it over a glass of wine, Miss Grey.'

And he marched her down the staircase and into the library.

CHAPTER TEN

THAT thudding of the door behind them was unusual for Luis, but then so was his expression and the violence with which he thrust forward a chair. But after he had gone round the desk and pressed a bell, and had waited till the huge silver tray set with decanters and glasses had been brought in, his fury seemed to settle into something calmer but more deadly.

He poured Madeira and handed her a glass, took his own down quickly and set the glass back upon the tray. He straightened, with his hands behind him.

'You have nothing at all to say?' he demanded. 'You act out this scene with Rico, knowing that I am well aware of what is happening, yet you have nothing whatever to say about it. Think, Miss Grey! Can you not find some pretty excuse for deceiving everyone? You have so far managed adequately in that direction. Surely this situation is not beyond you!'

Linda looked down at the cornelian-hued wine in her glass, was vaguely astonished that it remained so still while she shook so queerly inside.

'I know I owe you an explanation,' she began.

But this was too much for Luis. 'No, please! Do not disturb yourself, I beg you! Why should you explain to *me*?' He stalked across the room and back again. His teeth snapped. 'Let me first do some explaining, no? If I remember, you left your purse in my car the other night. I brought it to you and things were scattered, among them a small object which should never have been in your possession. I thought that over for some time, Miss Grey, and certain things became clear. I already knew that Rico was not with friends in Portão, but that charm he had given you told me that he had gone on a journey—because I knew his mother treasured it while he was in Brazil. It was obvious that you knew about his journey!'

'Yes, I knew,' she admitted quietly.

As if she had not spoken he went on. 'There was something else which puzzled me about two weeks ago. I had already made a request for some of the family jewels to be sent to me here. Then came this letter from my bank in Lisbon, asking if

153

I would consider it safer to have them sent here by air. I replied that in any case they could not come all the way to Merida because we have no airfield, and that the jewels must await my further instructions. The manager of the bank is a personal friend of mine, but he was away at the time, or I would have heard about the matter at once.' He paused, then said, 'So it was not difficult to work out this little business that night. Someone in Lisbon could have offered to bring the jewels by air—someone who would not surprise the bank by his knowledge of my affairs! Therefore, Rico was in Lisbon, with a plane at his disposal. I left for Lisbon at dawn!'

'That was Thursday morning,' she said involuntarily.

He nodded sharply. 'I could not trace Rico until today. It seems that to comply with regulations the plane had to be altered, and no one knew where these alterations were taking place. Also, the passengers had to be collected from different points. It was not till late this afternoon that I was informed the plane had left for Merida.'

'That must have been after it had crash-landed,' said Linda with a catch in her throat. 'Please believe me, senhor. I honestly thought he'd given up the idea.'

'But you agreed with it in the first place!' He leaned across the desk, his fingers spread wide apart as a support. 'All this was going on between you and Rico before he left and no one else was aware of it. It would not astonish me now to learn that you even knew of his plan to arrive here triumphantly with those jewels. Fortunately the bank manager returned from his holiday in time to prevent such idiocy!'

'But I gathered from Rico . . .'

He smiled angrily. 'Oh, yes, he brought a box from the bank—a few oddments from the waste basket carefully locked up! This bank manager, you see, has a sense of humour.' He swung round and stared at the book-lined wall. 'This unnatural behaviour in you pains me so much that I can hardly bear to talk about it. I will not believe that you are so infatuated with Rico that you would concur in anything he might plan, and treasure the medallion for him. Yet what else am I to believe?'

By this time Linda's emotions were so mixed that she hardly knew what she was thinking, let alone what to say. She took in a deep breath. 'It obviously pleased you very much to show me Juanita at Rico's bedside. You think you were right to refuse him the thing he wanted, but I still feel that he had to do this thing and fail, before he could settle here. I'm *not* infatuated with Rico.'

'Then how is it you have allowed so much to happen secretly between you?'

'None of it was of my seeking. You must have known that.'

'That was what I thought, at the start. But you were forbidden to see him; yet here we have you knowing all his plans, even down to his arrival here in a plane with passengers and certain freight! Both of you,' he said furiously, 'have defied the wishes of his mother and myself, and in order to do so you exchanged letters and must have met secretly and had discussions. Can you not possibly realise how I feel about this?'

A little unnerved by his rapid, alien-sounding English, the glittering eyes, Linda placed the drink she had scarcely sipped on the edge of the desk. The action, and the fact that there was some quality in his anger which had nothing to do with normal rage, helped her to take her time before answering.

'Please let me tell you what happened,' she said on a note of strain. 'The letter from Rico which you knew about was the only message that passed between us, and I didn't open it. It's probably still unopened in the pocket of the dress I wore that day. But apparently it was a request that I should meet Rico a little way down the road. I didn't turn up, of course, so he came here—to the nursery. Just in case of mishap, I think, he wanted someone here in the Palacio to know what he hoped to do, and there was no one else he could go to. I'm not superstitious, so holding the medallion for him till his return didn't mean anything to me.'

'But why did you not come to me at once?'

'I don't break confidence with people. And to be candid, I thought that if Rico really had it in him to go ahead with such a harebrained scheme he should have his chance.' She tacked on bitterly, 'In a way, things have turned out just as you wanted them to, but it wouldn't be like that if he hadn't tried this stunt of his and made a mess of it. He'd have been longing always to get away.'

'He could have lost his life on this stunt, as you call it.'

'He could probably have lost his life a thousand times while he was learning to fly in Brazil, but he didn't. He's the type to take risks without even recognising them, and the fact that he crash-landed doesn't mean he's not a good flier. Not that I'd tell him so,' she hastened to add, as Luis' jaw went taut. 'He's accepted Juanita in front of you and her mother, and he's too much a de Filano even to think of going back on his word. He'll probably marry her quite happily, like an obedient Portuguese son.'

Had there been no hurt in Linda she would have thought twice before uttering those final words; as it was, the moment they were spoken she felt a stab of regret so sharp that she couldn't look at him. She felt a handkerchief rip between her fingers and wondered how it had got there; her throat was as hot and raw as if 'flu were on the way.

His tones were cold and merciless. 'That was why I allowed the medallion to pass between you upstairs—so that he should marry the sort of girl who would be good for him. You will not believe that he is more than half in love with Juanita, but it is true. When he is well Rico will fling himself into this marriage as he flung himself into the sky; but a good marriage is permanent and steadying—at his age it is what he needs.' He paused, and then said abruptly, 'Drink your wine.'

'No, thanks.'

Still standing on the other side of the desk, he said, 'I understand you saw this thing happen out there in the pasture.'

She nodded, looking away from him. 'I'd just gone out with Mike Cullum. We both saw it and he raised the alarm in Merida.'

'And you lost your day with him.'

She nodded and stood up. 'Doña Velira mentioned that you want Jacinto to have a few weeks at the sea. You'll find someone else to go with him now, of course, but . . .'

'Why should I find someone else?' he asked sharply. 'Do you not care for the idea?'

'I can't stay on with him, after this,' she answered in low tones. 'Doña Velira will hate me, and you're like a . . . a . . .'

'A what?' he queried evenly.

'Like an enraged Marquez, I suppose,' she said on a sigh. 'I seem to have done everything I shouldn't, when all I really wanted was to mind my own business. I didn't want to hook up with the volatile personality of your cousin, and I certainly didn't intend to fall foul of the senhora.'

'You may be at rest about the senhora. Since Rico will now be officially engaged it will be easy to soothe her into forgetfulness of today's upheaval. I will see to it.' He had lost some of the hardness, but there was still something strange and calculating in his expression. 'It puzzles me how you can be so clever with children and so foolish with men.'

'Where men are concerned I haven't been trained to cope,' she said.

'Do you never look below the surface?'

She lifted her shoulders. 'You can't see more than a man chooses to reveal.'

'Yet you felt you knew Rico very well—till he philosophically yielded to circumstances this evening.'

'Rico is a problem child grown up. I've had dealings with the young of the species.'

'And Cullum. Do you feel you know him?'

'He's told me about himself and we've talked about things. Yes, I know him fairly well.'

'He is too fond of burdening others with his unhappiness, whatever it may be,' he said offhandedly. 'As an architect he should be studying the wealth of lovely buildings in Portugal, not feeding this misery of his in one small town. If he were not the brother of Eve Bayes ...' He broke off, then said noncommittally, 'I am the only other man you have known here, am I not? How far do you feel you understand me?'

She glanced at him briefly. 'It's difficult to say. You've been very kind, and you've given in over Jacinto much more than I thought you would; in fact, I believe it's only a matter of time before he'll get a good steel swing in the garden and a see-saw, and you might even put on a cartoon film for his fifth birthday. After that, it won't be such a long step to a pony of his own and a friend to ride with.'

He said, his voice grim and foreign, 'It seems you do not see me as a man at all.'

But that's the trouble, her heart cried; I do! Aloud, she replied, 'Well, naturally, there's part of you that's shuttered away from a person like me.' With a fatal calm she ended, 'Possibly it's something that only a Portuguese woman could understand.'

'I think you are right,' he said crisply. 'We will now go to dinner.'

She remember that Doña Velira was in her room, that the two Montales had probably gone their way. She looked at him with eyes that were unnaturally bright because she was forcing back the sting of tears.

'I'd prefer a tray in my room, if you don't mind.'

'We still have to discuss this visit to the sea,' he said curtly.

But she couldn't stand any more today. 'Can't we leave it for a while, senhor?'

However, there was one thing more she had to bear. There came the swift click of heels in the hall, the mere suggestion of a rap on the door panel, and Nolette came in, a mink stole draped across gleaming shoulders, the bodice of the black gown rising and falling with sweet agitation. She went straight to Luis and placed both hands on his arm.

'Oh, caro,' she murmured, vibrant with distress. 'I have only just heard about this frightful accident! We were invited into Portão for the whole day, Papa and I, and I was dressing for an evening at the Estrella when this news came in. I insisted on being driven here at once.' The hands clasped his arm more tightly. 'Is it true that Rico flew the plane himself? How is he?'

Luis' manner had changed; he was the courteous charmer, unwilling to have his womenfolk distressed; almost every trace of coolness was gone. 'It is over, my dear Nolette. Rico is in bed and sufficiently chastened.'

'I am so relieved,' she said on a quivering sigh. 'The rumours in Portão were so wild. It was even said that he made the flight expressly in order to bring you some jewels from Lisbon!' Though she was tall she had to look up several inches to meet his eyes. 'I told them that could not be true.'

'Not quite,' he said, smiling with narrow-eyed arrogance, as if his humour was now restored. His glance flickered over the neatly-uniformed Linda, and his hand came up to pat the white fingers which were locked on his sleeve. 'I brought the jewels with me, Nolette, and you must come to lunch tomorrow and see them. We must get out a design for the new settings.'

'I cannot wait!' Nolette exclaimed softly. She turned slightly and only then, it seemed, became aware of Linda. 'Oh, Miss Grey! What have you done with poor Michael? Eve has no guests this evening—he will be inconsolable without you.'

'I doubt it,' said Linda, still burning from an irrational flare of hate. 'Will you excuse me?'

'Oh, but you have quarrelled with Michael,' Nolette said sympathetically. 'I was afraid it would happen. Luis, my dear,' she turned upon him large remorseful eyes for a moment, 'quite unwittingly I have spoiled this little romance. I should not have permitted Mr Cullum to come so often to

158

the studio. It has made Miss Grey jealous, and I am terribly sorry. But, Miss Grey, I assure you that I share only one interest with your Mike. You must forgive him his neglect.'

'Please excuse me, senhor!' said Linda, and she went out and almost banged the door.

She ran up to her room and lit a cigarette, clasped her arms across her waist and walked out on to the balcony and back again. She wouldn't endure any more of this! Let Luis have his Nolette and Rico his Juanita. She was just Linda Grey, who was totally out of place here anyway. No use telling herself she had fallen in love with the wrong man; far better to knock into her head the fact that she had not fallen in love at all. No self-respecting English girl should go starry-eyed over a man who obviously was unaware of her except as someone who looked after his son and whom he could bait occasionally. Love Luis? Why, she detested him!

She jammed out the cigarette in an ashtray, pushed shaking fingers through the cornsilk hair. The door opened and a trolley was wheeled in by a manservant.

She said, 'Just leave the coffee and take the rest away, will you?'

'The Senhor Marquez ordered it,' he told her persuasively. 'He said I must bring it up at once.'

'I'm not hungry. Please take it away, and if you have to explain to him . . .'

'No, senhora, it will not be necessary to explain. The Senhor Marquez has gone out.'

She knew the answer before she asked, 'Do you know where he's gone?'

The man bowed. 'To the Estrella in Portão. Dinner is served there till midnight.'

'With . . . with Senhorita del Carros?'

'But naturally,' he replied, and disappeared with the trolley.

She drank black coffee and smoked another cigarette. She thought of Rico peacefully sleeping now that he had proved himself not quite the man he had thought he was, and of Juanita at last serene. She thought of Doña Velira unconscious from a sedative but awakening tomorrow with a sense of pride and victory. She visualised the jewels placed against Nolette's exquisite skin, that mouth which was a work of art clinging to Luis'. And she remembered the quick shock of emotion each time she, Linda Grey, found herself alone with the Marquez. And each of the things she thought was less bearable than the last. She couldn't possibly carry on here. It might be better at the summer villa, but even that. . . .

Driven by a desperate restlessness, she wandered to the communicating door and slipped through into the darkened bedroom where Jacinto slept. She went to the bed and stood there till her vision accustomed itself to the pale radiance filtering through the vent window. She saw Jacinto's small face, untroubled on the pillow, his dark hair which was surprisingly cool and crisp to the touch. Each night he took something to bed with him, and tonight he had chosen the book she had given him on his birthday, the one which opened up to reveal the horsemen and the fort and the battleship in a series of stage scenes. She recalled that last night he had clutched some drawings she had made for him, and the night before she had found a powder case from her dressing table on his pillow.

She straightened up and took a long breath, felt cool air drawn deeply into her lungs. Well, she had to come to terms with it. Jacinto would go on needing her till someone else took her place. It hurt to love a man like Luis, a man who was from another world, with an other-world taste in women, but she had to stay with Jacinto till the hurt drove her away.

But upon one thing she was decided. Till she and Jacinto left for the summer villa she would live her life quite apart from Luis and Doña Velira, Nolette and even Mike. No more trying to please the old senhora by keeping Mike away from Nolette; no more talks with any of them. Let them work out their own problems.

And supposing, a voice whispered, the engagement of Nolette and Luis is announced this week—what then? Linda had no answer. She simply found herself remembering that two or three times lately she had wanted to weep, yet had remained dry-eyed. Tonight it was just the same—a hot heavy ache, a faint stinging. Perhaps it wasn't yet time for tears.

There was much coming and going on Sunday. The Montales family were ceremoniously received at lunch by an almost recovered Doña Velira. Nolette came with her father and Mike came along with Eve and John Bayes. There was talk at the end of lunch about an adjournment to the library, where Luis would display the jewels, but Linda refused the invitation to accompany the others and went straight out into the grounds for a long walk. When she returned the Palacio was quiet, except in Rico's bedroom, where several of his friends had gathered to drink wine with him and discuss his exploit; their laughter echoed through the open door and along to the landing. Plainly, even if the intended reward had eluded Rico, he was gleaning its remnants. Good luck to him.

Linda made tea in the nursery, played with Jacinto and took him down to the kennel. When they came in she inclined her head politely to Luis in the hall, and when he spoke to the child she crossed to the foot of the stairs, and waited. She had seen the cold dark look in Luis' face and steeled herself not to care.

She did not go down again that day, and the next morning she paid the last visit with Jacinto to the studio. Mike did not turn up, and Linda asked pointedly if she might sit in the balcony with a book. Later, she saw the finished head and had to admit it was good and would look better still in bronze. Not that Nolette cared for her opinion. The Portuguese woman had gained some bright heaven where her work seemed to matter very little.

'It is not likely that I shall do very much more of this,' she remarked as she went with them to the door. 'It is an enchanting hobby, but I have always felt it is hardly dignified to take commissions, and now, of course, they are out of the question. Is it yet decided which day you will go to the sea, Miss Grey?'

'I haven't been told.'

'It will almost certainly be Saturday or Sunday. I think Luis will find it good to have the Palacio to himself.'

'Possibly.'

The black eyebrows rose, the red mouth curved with amusement. 'You are still angry with Mr Cullum?'

'I was never angry with him, and you know it.'

Nolette shrugged. 'I confess I find you difficult to understand. Mr Cullum is comparatively simple and there are similarities between you two, but he has not this independence of thought and speech which I find very trying. Luis will have it that you are good for the boy, but in time I think you will have him noisy and demanding freedom.'

'Freedom is the natural element of the child,' said Linda.

'Well, we shall see.' A pause. 'I think it would help us all if you went back to England. If you yourself were to decide this, Luis would dissuade you because so far he likes your way with Jacinto. It would be better if your father were to write asking Luis to release you.'

161

Linda took Jacinto's hand and began to walk down the steps to the car. She looked back and asked, 'Why are you so sure I won't tell the senhor what you've suggested?'

Nolette gave the low husky laugh. 'I have suggested nothing that is not for your own good. I have already told Luis that you are out of your setting and he agrees. Adeus, Jacinto!'

Linda was not perturbed, only a little weary of it all. And as the days passed it seemed that the weariness would cling for ever. She developed the habit of speaking at lunch and dinner only if she was addressed, and then in the smallest number of words. She never entered the sala except to go into the grounds, and if Jacinto was needed there to meet some visitor she sent him in alone. Once or twice Doña Velira had tried to speak to her privately, but she had said point blank that she was interested only in anything concerning Jacinto, and the senhora had retired, ruffled but oddly subdued.

On Wednesday evening, while Jacinto was eating supper, Rico came to the nursery. He wore tight-waisted black trousers and a floppy silk shirt which had had part of the shoulder cut away to accommodate the huge dressing, and he came in smiling the ravishing white smile and holding up crossed fingers.

'Pax! This is right, no?' He made a pass over Jacinto's eyes, laughed when the child blinked. 'How are you, my little rabbit? You have missed Rico?'

'Did you really fly the plane?'

Rico laughed delightedly. 'He knows! I am a brave big cousin, eh, Jacinto?'

'Will you take me in the plane?'

'Oh, come,' said Linda, frowning pointedly at Rico. 'This is supper-time. Rico is not allowed in the nursery.'

'You are wrong, my dear Linda. I am a betrothed man and therefore discreet to the point of boredom. I come to tell you that I still love my two little rabbits in here. It was sad that my courageous plan, about which we took so much pains, should have gone wrong, but I am told that every failure has its compensations. I now have the Montales!'

'You mustn't talk like that. It's . . . it's horrid.'

'But they are not too bad, these Montales,' he told her encouragingly, as if she were the one who needed bolstering for marriage. 'Before, I could not see Juanita for the plane in the sky, but now I think she is as sweet as my mother says. She will obey me, Linda, which you would not!'

'There was never any question of my having to obey you!'

'No,' he said, and added consideringly and with sincerity, 'but there is something you have—a spirit and a certain look about you—which a man can need very much. I have never seen you look at a man with love, but when you do, that man will adore you for the rest of his life.'

'Nonsense,' she said abruptly. 'Your bruises have nearly disappeared. How is the shoulder?'

'Better, but the big bandage brings me a pleasant amount of fussing. I shall keep it till Friday, when we have our engagement party.'

'So you're having a function?'

'A big one. Luis insists, for Juanita's sake. He has a way with Juanita—makes her feel important and much wanted. It is strange, because me, I think, he would like to ship back to Brazil!'

'Well, there's nothing strange about *that*. I expect he loathes the sight of the plane in the Valle das Flores.'

'It is not a pretty sight, I daresay, but it will not be there for long. Already he has mechanics at work on it and it will leave tomorrow or Friday. I am afraid the business will cost him a considerable sum because the man who owns the plane is disappointed that he is not to be a colleague of the Marquez de Filano; he will therefore run up the bills, as you say. It is poor luck that it should have finished like this.'

Seeing that he still appeared blithe, Linda answered, 'You were lucky to come through so well. You didn't deserve to.'

'Those are hard words from a pretty mouth!' He turned to Jacinto, who still sat at the table. 'She is tender at heart, menino. It is only when a girl is hurt that she speaks sharply.'

'Please,' said Linda. 'You may advise him on such matters when he's a little older.'

'By then, perhaps, there will be a small Rico to share the education,' he said cheerfully. 'You will come to our party on Friday, of course.'

She bent to give Jacinto a clean plate for his fruit. 'I don't think so, Rico, thanks. I don't know many of the people and I haven't the right dress for it.'

'But I insist!' he said warmly. 'It would be no engagement if you were not there. I tell you, Linda! Buy a new dress, very Portuguese, and I will get you some combs.' He looked critically at her hair. 'But not too easy to use combs with such short curls, eh? You will get the dress, though?'

'It's good of you, Rico, but I'd feel far happier up here. I mean it.'

'I mean it, too,' he said doggedly. 'You do not come, I lift Cain!'

She smiled. 'One raises Cain, and I still say no. I wouldn't enjoy it.'

He looked at her, saw her turn her face to avoid his stare, and said softly, 'It is that English oaf?'

She tried to smile again. 'That's hardly the way to refer to a man who's been your friend. And don't couple me with him, either; I've had enough of it.'

'But there is someone?' he urged. 'Someone who makes you unhappy?'

'I'm just tired and busy—we're going to the coast at the weekend. And now let Jacinto finish his supper in peace.'

He watched her peel and quarter the child's apple, said slowly, 'I have not the subtle mind, but also I am not entirely the fool. The other night, when you brought the St Francis—Luis was there and he said nothing.'

'I suppose he had nothing to say. Please go, Rico.'

'But you were frightened; I saw in your face the fear, and I felt it in your hand.'

'Well, I hadn't ever practised palming a medal on to someone else. I was bound to be nervous.'

'You are being flippant,' he sighed. 'I do not know why you find it so impossible to speak of yourself. I have told you everything about me from the first day we met in the library.'

'Too much,' she managed quite firmly. 'I congratulate you on your engagement to Juanita and hope you will make her a model husband.'

'And you will not tell me what it is that paints the shadows in those very blue eyes?'

'I've told you—I'm just tired.' To Jacinto she said, 'Say goodnight to Rico, darling.'

Rico shrugged again, half humorously and half with exasperation. He bent and lightly kissed Jacinto's forehead, and Linda thought, achingly, that she had never seen Luis perform that simple act with the child. She went with Rico to the door.

He said, 'Our guests are asked for eight-thirty on Friday and dinner will be served at nine. If you wish, do not come down till nine o'clock.'

'I'm sorry, but I can't be there. I've only one evening dress with me and it isn't suitable.'

164

'What is the colour?'

'White.'

He exploded the tips of his fingers near his lips. 'Enchanting! You will tear my heart.'

'I shan't come down.'

'Will you come at ten, after dinner?' he begged.

'Just forget me, please!'

'That is impossible,' he said simply. 'You must drink a toast to us or for me the occasion will be ruined.'

'Don't exaggerate. I'll drink it up here.'

'I cannot bring Juanita up here from our party!' He ignored the fact that she was almost closing the door on him. 'Do this for me, Linda. The small sala will not be in use, and I will bring Juanita there at ten o'clock. We will wait for you, but do not be late because we shall not be able to stay away from the others for very long. And as it is a great occasion for Juanita and me, will you wear the white dress?'

'Yes,' she said resignedly. 'Take your foot away or I'll squash it in the door!'

She heard him laugh after the door was closed, marvelling at his resilience. It seemed that all he had needed to put him right was an absolute failure. In a way, Luis and Doña Velira had been right about him; in another way, she had been right herself. It was merely that they knew one side of Rico and she the other. He seemed to be all set for happy days.

CHAPTER ELEVEN

It was cool and cloudy next morning, and for the first time since her arrival at the Palacio, Linda wore a cashmere cardigan over her uniform. She looked up the lesson marked a week ago by Doña Velira and found that this morning she should impart a little botany. But it seemed too ridiculous to insist upon a four-year-old's attention to printed details about the agave and the prickly pear, and she decided that if in order to be able to answer his aunt's questions he had to learn about growing things he should do it outdoors and without books. She knew where there were both agaves and prickly pears.

To get to them, they had to walk down the side track used by the mule carts loading in the orchards. This excursion in itself provided Jacinto with much interest, for peach picking was in progress, and village boys with donkey carts were permitted to gather the fallen fruit and take it home. Later in the week an aura of peach brandy would emanate from the poorer cottages.

They reached the side gate where a porter regulated the desultory flow of mule and donkey traffic, went out on to the road and trod a footpath in the verge. And presently they came to a high bank where ragged agave roots swung in the breeze and the long, spear-shaped leaves were cupped here and there round single flower trunks which reached a height of twenty or thirty feet.

She fabricated a story about a child who planted an agave when he was five and watched it grow all through his life, till it flowered when he was seventy—flowered once and then died. And inwardly she seethed a little that the facts of an agave's life, however singular, should be thought necessary to his education at the age of four. She put him up on the bank and climbed up there with him. There were plenty of prickly pears, and they, thank goodness, were obviously queer oval green plates with spikes on them and the odd habit of growing out of the top of each other. Jacinto already knew them well because he had been warned a hundred times against touching the deadly prickles.

He was actually more absorbed in the distant windmills

with their canvas sails flapping and twirling, and for a while they sat on the grass watching them and chanting the Portuguese alphabet and p-a-o spells bread. Linda knew that Doña Velira would already have prepared lessons for the seaside, but she also knew that once she and Jacinto were away from the Palacio she would please herself what she taught him and how she did it. It would be a sort of last fling, for quite certainly she would never come back here; it was something she accepted fatalistically.

'I want to see the plane,' he said.

'Perhaps later on you'll see it go up in the sky,' she answered, and she looked at his small eager face and thought of the rather dead-pan child he had been when she arrived.

Jacinto as she had first known him would never have stated one of his wants; he had never even presumed to have any, just as he had never admitted even to himself that he wanted a puppy, or to clamber up the hills, or to go without a tie. He had never even sought maternal affection from anyone till she had shown him what it was, and now she was becoming afraid that she had awakened in him a need which nobody would fill. With Nolette, he would be forced to get painfully back into his shell; far better had his young emotions been left dormant.

'It's getting towards lunch-time,' she said. 'We'll have to go.'

He stood up obediently and gave her his hand. She pretended he had pulled her up and thanked him politely, and he laughed and pressed his nose against her skirt. She went first and slithered down the bank, turned with upstretched arms. It was when she had him in a tricky position that she heard the car stop on the road behind her, so she stayed there, taking his weight till he slipped down into her arms. She turned about and found Luis there, felt Jacinto taken from her and set down on the grass.

The child said at once, 'We watched the windmills, Papa.'

'So?' said Luis without interest. He looked at Linda. 'We have not yet had the talk about your visit to the coast. You have been avoiding me.'

She replied offhandedly, 'You could have sent for me, senhor. I've been expecting it.'

'I do not wish to order you to do anything. This is a thing we must discuss as equals.'

'I don't see how that's possible—but when do you want to see me?'

'Let us walk a little,' he said abruptly. 'Jacinto can wait in the car.'

'Please let him run ahead. He's not out with you often enough, and he loves this feeling of you being just behind, and watching him.'

'Have your way,' he shrugged. 'We will take this path through the trees.' They were among the wild lemon and olives, when he added, 'You will like the summer villa. I will send servants with you, and the old caretaker and his wife are completely trustworthy. The beach is very safe, and you will be ... mistress there. The place is only seventy miles from Merida, and you will have a car at your disposal, so you will not feel isolated.'

'I see.'

'I myself will come out occasionally to see you, but I am very anxious that you should not feel lonely.'

'With the sea outside and a free hand as far as Jacinto is concerned, I shan't be lonely.'

He walked in silence for a moment, then: 'Jacinto means more to you than any of us, no?'

'He has to, doesn't he?' she replied non-committally. 'He's the reason I'm here.'

'That is so, but one doesn't lose oneself entirely in a child who belongs to someone else.'

He had spoken deliberately and she cast him a swift glance. He looked stern.

'I'm fond of Jacinto for himself,' she said. 'He's a normal child, really, and in any case children are my job.'

He left the subject. 'The villa is large,' he said. 'As well as the family apartments, which you will occupy, there are eight guest rooms. This is the holiday season in England, is it not? It is my intention to write to your father, inviting him and your stepmother to spend some time with you at the villa. I would already have written, but ...' He broke off in a way which was unlike Luis. Then he went on, 'There is no reason why they should not bring friends, if they wish—the happier for you if they do, perhaps.'

'But I don't want my parents there,' said Linda, in a voice gone cold with apprehension. 'I don't doubt that your intentions are kindly, senhor, but I'm very glad you haven't written before speaking to me.'

'What are your objections?' he demanded.

She could have said, 'One doesn't let one's parents in on an unhappy love affair. It's the sort of nightmare one lives down inside oneself without telling a soul.' But she didn't, of course. Instead, she looked down at the leaf-strewn grass. 'I can't give my reasons. Isn't it enough that I don't want them?'

'It is unnatural.'

'Not really. In England we have family conventions, just as you do. I love my father and I'm fond of my stepmother, but I don't mix them in with my job. It was a generous impulse, senhor, but please forget it.'

'So you now admit,' he said, with a smile in which a dash of intolerance was blended with cynicism, 'that I am capable of acting upon impulse. Yet in this case it was not an impulse. I have thought for some time it would be a good plan for you and your family to be together for a while, and from your point of view the family atmosphere might help Jacinto. I feel strongly about this invitation to your people.'

'So do I,' she said firmly, her glance still lowered. 'I'm awfully afraid that any invitation you may extend to my father will automatically become my resignation from your employment.'

He drew a breath that she heard above the rustle of leaves in the wind. 'That infernal independence! How is one to combat it? How can I make you see that I want nothing but your good? Always I come up against this—this uncharacteristic hardness in you that I cannot understand!'

Perhaps it was forturnate for Linda just then that she noticed Jacinto's disappearance. Her temples were throbbing and her vision blurred, but she ran forward.

'Jacinto!' she called. 'Where are you?'

She stood very still, heard a small shout of laughter overhead and saw him well up in the very tree under which she had paused; he was at least fifteen feet above the ground. Beside her, Luis said, 'My faith!' under his breath, but before he could move she had unconsciously gripped his wrist, gripped it so tightly that he must have stayed there in astonishment, if for no other reason.

Her heart thudding in her throat, her breathing almost halted, Linda watched the small figure descend the tree, saw the shiny black shoes feel for the gnarled branches of the olive and take firm hold before he came lower. He arrived at a point where Luis could have lifted him down, but as she felt a

movement beside her her fingers tightened of their own voli-
tion, and he stood there simply looking on, till the child had
reached the ground and turned upon them victoriously.

Linda felt faint, but she managed a mild, 'That was a little
too high, darling, but very good.'

The child said excitedly, 'I climbed the tree, Papa. You saw
me!'

'Yes,' he said oddly. 'I saw you.'

The child's face fell. 'You do not think it was clever?'

'It was clever, but you do not climb so high again. You
understand?' He waved back towards the car. 'I will take you
home now.'

Jacinto went ahead, crestfallen. Luis lifted his hand, looked
at the two tiny crescents of blood her nails had drawn on his
wrist.

'Was there need for such intensity? Had he fallen I would
have caught him.'

'I . . . I'm terribly sorry. I didn't realise what I was doing.
You see, I so badly wanted him to do it himself, quite alone.
He's been practising on a low tree for the express purpose of
showing off to you. You happened to be here and he couldn't
find a low one. Perhaps he even chose the high spot deliberately, because your approval means so much to him.' She
paused, drew in her lip and said, low-voiced, 'You didn't even
show him you were pleased.'

Luis let several seconds elapse before he said, in a savage
undertone, 'I am supposed to understand the workings of
your mind and his. I am also expected to comprehend everything else that you do! You do not mind that I am angered or
hurt, so long as your little tricks for other people are successful.' More coolly, he said, 'I believe I know why you are unhappy, menina. At the sea you will forget these things. Come!'

He put them in the car and drove through the side gateway
and up into the orchards, where only a couple of carts remained. He swept round and on to the drive, and with a tight
expression he helped them out. Luis went first up the steps
and opened the main door. They all entered the hall.

Rico was coming down the staircase and he hailed them
gaily. 'Bom dias, my children. How is it with you?'

Jacinto said politely, 'Bom dias. I go to wash for lunch.'

'So sad? Or are you hungry, my little squirrel?'

His smile as taut as his voice, Luis said, 'The child is tired.
He has been doing brave deeds this morning. Only ten

170

minutes ago he climbed high in a tree. It was a magnificent performance.'

Jacinto looked a long way up at Luis and smiled, at first uncertainly and then more happily. To Rico he said, 'I will climb a tree for you, but only a little tree.'

'That is unfair!' declared Rico. 'Just because your father has more inches he has the big tree. No matter—perhaps I will climb a mulberry bush for you instead.'

In cold tight tones, Luis said, 'Take the boy upstairs, Miss Grey. As you have had a long walk you may prefer to lunch in the nursery.'

'Very well, senhor.'

He glittered at her. 'I am not instructing you. You choose for yourself.'

Rico raised an eyebrow and said nothing. Linda sighed, and took Jacinto's hand.

'We'll lunch upstairs, thank you, senhor.'

Linda had never felt so racked and restless. She saw Jacinto down for his afternoon rest and went back to the nursery. She tried to read, but it was hopeless, and she couldn't settle to sewing, either. At last she tidied up and went downstairs to ask one of the servants if she could have the use of the car. It was brought round and she was driven down into Merida.

The town at this hour was dead, but she left the car parked at the market square and walked along the narrow cobbled streets and out towards the avenidas. But about a hundred yards from the del Carros quinta she turned back. The thought of seeing Nolette sent snakes up her spine. She found a pavement café which was deserted except for the somnolent owner, and she sat down at one of the tables and looked at the line of small shops on the other side of the street. As so often happens in the towns of Portugal, there was a tall, dignified house squashed in between two shops which impartially displayed silks and trinkets and groceries. Above a studded oak door a faience name-tile in blue and white said 'Casa de Dom Antonio Fereniz'.

Linda had never before noticed the house, but it reminded her of some she had seen on the drive through Lisbon on the day of her arrival. She thought of Lisbon, the palm-lined squares and avenidas, the splendid buildings and the Tagus, and she wondered if she would have felt better had the Palacio been nearer to a really big city. Not better, she thought; she would only have had less opportunity for intro-spection.

The café owner woke up, blinked at her and came to attention. 'You would like wine, senhora?' he asked in Portuguese.

'Chocolate, please,' she said, 'and some of the small pastries.'

By the way he gazed at her and hurried to obey, she knew that he connected her with the Palacio. Reflected glory, and it was not very sweet. The pastries looked delicious, so did the glass of chocolate in its metal holder, but she hardly touched either. She remembered telling herself defiantly that she would do just this—sit at an outdoor table and order chocolate and cakes. But it hadn't the taste of triumph. She paid the bill, saw that a few people had stirred into the streets and knew it was time to return to the Palacio.

She was on her way to the market square when Eve Bayes leaned from a car window and called her. The car was parked outside Merida's biggest store and was apparently ready to move off.

Eve opened the back door and looked out. 'Can I take you somewhere?'

'No, thanks. The state carriage is waiting for me at the market square. Isn't it unusual for you to come to Merida on a Thursday?'

Eve nodded, pushed the door wider. 'Come and sit in with me. I want a word with you.' After Linda was seated, she indicated the driver with a glance. 'He doesn't understand English, so don't mind what you say. I never seem to see you alone. How are you doing?'

'I'm not an unqualified success, but circumstances have been against me. I may do better at the coast.'

'Yes, I heard you were going. As a matter of fact,' even though it was unnecessary, Eve lowered her voice, 'Senhora de Filano came to see me this morning. She wrote me on Luis' behalf inviting John and me to Rico's engagement party tomorrow night, and she tacked on a request that I would arrive today so that she could see me. Even in the letter she said she would like to call on me at eleven this morning. I was agog, of course. The old lady always summons people to see her, she never calls except on relatives. So I wondered.'

Linda was wondering, too. 'Probably she didn't want anyone at the Palacio to see you.'

'Exactly—she didn't. It took her some time to come to the

172

point, and I couldn't hurry her, because I hadn't the vaguest idea what it was all about.'

'I think I know,' said Linda. 'Your brother.'

Eve's shoulders lifted. 'So there's really something in it? I'll admit it's occurred to me, and I even warned Mike, but I didn't imagine it was serious. I told Doña Velira that I couldn't believe Mike would attract a woman like Nolette against her judgment. She said, rather grandly, that it wasn't a case of attraction, not on Nolette's side, anyway. The fact that Mike's my brother and living here meant that he had to be invited often to the Palacio. Also, we're only a few houses from the del Carros', and Mike has the English disregard of the proprieties. She said that Luis is obviously unhappy about it. Apparently he's so much in love with Nolette that he can't bear another man to look at her.'

A trifle thinly, Linda said, 'Luis hinted to me himself that if Mike wasn't your brother he'd get rid of him.'

Eve looked worried. 'Really? It was too bad of Mike! I never knew him to take much interest in women before, but here in Merida he seems to have divided his attentions between you and Nolette del Carros. He's been most peculiar altogether, moody at one moment and happy the next. I hate to say it, but I'm glad he's gone.'

'Gone?' echoed Linda. 'You mean he's left Merida?'

'He came in as Doña Velira was leaving, and when she'd left he made some facetious remark about the mountain coming to Mahomet. So I told him what she'd come for. He looked fed up for a bit and then said he'd pack up and go. He drove off straight after lunch.'

'Didn't you have a proper talk with him?'

'I tried, but he wouldn't answer. As he left, he said, "Tell Linda I'm sorry I didn't have time to say goodbye." I asked him where he was going, and he shrugged and said he'd probably go to Spain and then home. And that was all.'

'Poor Mike!'

'It was his own fault,' stated his sister, a shade tartly. 'Even before Nolette arrived I told him that she was coming to marry Luis. Her father hinted at it several times, and Doña Velira had told me, too. I think Mike must move with a bohemian crowd in England.'

'It's not particularly bohemian to be friendly with an unmarried woman. After all,' it was not even a shred of comfort now but she had to say it, 'Luis and Nolette are not engaged.'

173

'No, but the old lady suggested that it was possible the announcement would be made tomorrow night, perhaps at the end of the party. Everything points that way—those jewels, getting the child away to the sea. There's even talk, it seems, of a small house on one of the avenidas for Doña Velira. I don't think Luis sanctions the rumours, but he doesn't suppress them.'

'I still think it's hard on Mike.' But Eve seemed so to have lost touch with her brother that she would never understand how he had felt after the loss of that girl in England, even if Linda could have told her. 'Doña Velira will be glad to hear he's gone,' she added.

'Yes. Will you tell her for me? No details; just say he's left for home.'

'We've had so many little bothers that I've sworn off taking an interest in the family's affairs.'

'Well, do this for me, there's a dear. It's safer than sending a note, and I'd like to be sure it's all settled today.' She paused. 'Do you find it tiring to live all the while with Portuguese?'

'Perhaps deflating is the word.'

'Then why not come down for dinner tonight with John and me? We'd love to have you.'

'Thanks very much, but I always leave someone on duty, and they're so busy with preparations for tomorrow that I can't ask them to spare a servant for our quarters. But . . . but I would like to beg a favour.'

'Go right ahead. I realise now that I left you far too much to Mike's untender mercies. What can I do for you, Linda?'

'It's . . . tomorrow night.' Linda found herself growing slightly incoherent, and pulled herself up. With an effort she made her tones casual. 'I'm not going to the party.'

'No? But you've been so easily accepted by everyone. I thought you'd be bound to be there!'

'To be honest, I don't fancy it—not at all. Luis has a bit of a down on me at the moment, and when he's like that he's always more polite and considerate, in a leashed way. I don't know many of the people, and I do want to keep out of the way of the family, but he'll insist in my attending—if I'm at the Palacio.' She stopped, and then asked, 'What time will you turn up there?'

'Eight-thirty.'

Linda hesitated. 'Do you think your chauffeur could take

174

me back to your house for an hour or so? I promised Rico that I'd have a drink with him and Juanita at ten o'clock, and after that I can go to bed without argument.'

Eve leaned back slightly, and looked at her. 'What a queer request. Is there something wrong?'

Linda shook her head. 'If you'll let me spend some time just reading in your sitting-room I'll be saved some wear and tear on the nerves, that's all. I swear that's all it means.'

'My dear girl, you may do as you like in the house. It's only that . . . Oh, well, I suppose you know what you're doing. I must admit I wouldn't like to be at odds with Luis, these days; he can be terse even under that charm. Don't expect me to make excuses to him for you.'

'No, please don't! If he sends up to the nursery and I'm not there he'll think I'm in the grounds; he'll have other things to worry about, anyway. He certainly won't mention anything about me to the guests, but he's an arrogant man. He can't bear to be crossed, or refused anything. Even when he gives in you have a feeling that he's won.'

Eve said slowly, 'You seem to have got to know him awfully well. I wonder if he knows as much about you?'

'I doubt it. Then you'll let me do as I suggest tomorrow night?'

She nodded, but cautiously. 'The very last thing I want is trouble with Luis. He does business with John and we can't afford to upset him. If I'm approached, I shall say you asked if you could use the car for an hour. I do have your word that you've nothing rash in mind?'

'Of course! My whole aim is to keep out of trouble.'

'Well, see you do. If you slip up anywhere don't expect help from me. I'm only doing this for you because you're English and perhaps because I'm a scrap conscience-smitten over Mike.'

Linda smiled faintly. 'Whatever your reason, thanks a lot. Are you going past the market square?'

Eve gave the driver the order, and the car jolted over the cobbles, turned a corner and stopped opposite the Palacio car. Linda opened the door and closed it after her.

Through the window, Eve said, 'Don't forget my message to Doña Velira, will you? I'll leave out some coffee and maga-zines for you tomorrow night!'

Linda went back to the Palacio, found it more bustling than usual. Something was being done to the lighting in the large

175

sala, and rococo chairs with damask seats were being brought in from the store-room. The bedrooms nearest the head of the stairs were being prepared as powder rooms for the ladies, and a maid was marshalling vases and bowls inside another room. At the end of the corridor Jacinto leaned against the wall in his underwear watching operations; for him, this was daring, and she shooed him back into the bedroom with a playful smack. The time would come, she knew, when he would bring one of the puppies indoors; he would probably form the reprehensible habit at the summer villa.

She found herself shrinking from all reflection about the villa at the coast. Time enough for that when she arrived there.

She dined downstairs that night. Because of tomorrow's festivities there were no guests, and she sat at the long table with Doña Velira, Luis and Rico. There was very little conversation, and Luis did not address her directly at all. Even Rico seemed unable to break down the barrier.

When Doña Velira rose, Linda did the same. She felt Luis' presence as he escorted them to the door, but was glad to be in the small sala without him. She saw Doña Velira seated, waited till the usual adjustments were made and the hooded eyes looked up at her.

'Senhora,' she said clearly, 'I saw Mrs Bayes in town this afternoon. She asked me to tell you that Mr Cullum has already left Merida and is going home.'

The parchment-like face smiled, the combs nodded with satisfaction. 'That is good. Thank you, my child.'

'You will excuse me? Goodnight, senhora.'

'Do not go for a moment. I have nothing awkward to ask of you now, and I would like you to sit with me. On the stool, here. I wish to look into your face.'

Linda teetered, sank down on to the stool in a position from which she could quickly escape. 'Yes, senhora?'

'I feel happy tonight, because all the things I have wished for are coming to pass. My son is to settle here near us at last, and Luis is going to get his heart's desire. Rico is ordinarily a merry soul and he is not likely to be troubled with regrets for that foolish flying. Luis is different.' Meditatively, she tapped a finger on the arm of her chair. 'For Luis, one can only wish that he will marry the woman he loves. Nothing less will do for him, nothing less will make him truly happy.'

'I agree, senhora. Is that all?'

176

'You are impatient. It seems to me it does not occur to you that my time here at the Palacio is coming to an end, and I may need some solace. One can be uplifted by events and still need consolation for one's age and loneliness.'

'I've never thought of you as lonely, Doña Velira.'

She gave a foreign shrug, smiled the eagle-like smile. 'It is not so much a loneliness. One does not like to feel useless. You have not cared for my guidance of the senhorito, but anything I have done for him has been prompted from the heart.'

'I'm sure of that.'

'We cannot all,' with heavy but well-meant sarcasm, 'be trained at Rawson Hall! However, when you come back from the sea I do not want you to neglect me. Wherever I may be living, you must bring Jacinto to see me. And we will hope that the sea air will bring back the roses to your cheeks.'

There was practically nothing that Linda could reply to this, so she merely said conventionally, 'I'm quite well, senhora. May I bring your sewing?'

'You do not care to converse with the old woman, há?'

'It isn't that. I want to relieve the maid upstairs so that she can get a good night's rest. They'll all be busy tomorrow.'

'True, but I do not quite believe your excuse. However, I may try to visit you at the coast, when we will have more chance of talking. I myself shall not stay up late tonight, so I shall not need my sewing, but you may call Lupe. If she has not finished the ornamentation of that dress of mine, it must wait till tomorrow morning. Goodnight, pequena.'

Linda answered her quietly, went out to find Lupe, and then sent the corridor maid to bed. She got into her pyjamas and moved out into the balcony, and for a while she stood there with the cool breeze playing over the silk. The clouds were dispersing and stars shone in patches against an indigo backcloth.

Tomorrow Rico would be officially engaged, his future more or less assured. Mike had gone wandering back to England, perhaps slightly happier than he had come, but disgruntled none the less. She had the feeling that if he had come heartwhole to Merida he would have found even more to admire in Nolette del Carros.

The smell of cigar smoke drifted upwards, and she leant forward. She saw the tall figure in the immaculate dinner jacket, a thin radiance shining over the dark head. He was

177

alone, and thoughtful. His head lifted slightly, and she stepped back quickly into her room. It was like a small death, a preparation for stepping out of his life.

CHAPTER TWELVE

IT was so many years since Merida had known a really big affair at the Palacio that Rico's engagement party had assumed gigantic importance during the course of that week. As the function had been arranged rather quickly only friends and relations who lived within fifty miles had been invited, but it was thought that the guests would number more than a hundred. Which surely meant that when the Marquez announced his own marriage an even greater number would gather!

As was usual, the relatives arrived first, at about eight. There was Rico's elder brother and his wife, his sister and her husband, a few aunts, uncles and cousins, most of them distantly related to the Marquez. And there were the Montales' connections, an elegant sedate crowd with Juanita in their midst.

As Rico told her the moment they met, Juanita looked charming in her black taffeta dress and silver lace stole, with a camellia in her hair. If he had felt any regret at the departure of the plane it had not lasted long, for tonight he could see only the brilliant, illuminated grandeur of the Palacio, the fiery gold plate, the scintillating chandeliers, the footmen carrying rich wines with as much pleasure as the guests were drinking them . . . and the girl who was sweet to make love to and beautifully accomplished in the home. When he had first returned from Brazil he had laughed at the thought of placing a ring on Juanita's finger, but only two days ago he had found himself doing it tenderly. He did love the little thing; the idea of flying had got in the way, that was all. Rico's was not a complex nature.

At eight-thirty, when those outside the family circles began to arrive, Rico stood in the hall with Doña Velira and Juanita, her parents and Luis, to greet them. Old Dom Josef and his daughter, the Gonzales, the Moreiras, John and Eve Bayes, the Texeiras, Jorge Perez and his parents. They kept coming, offering their felicitations and passing into the grand sala.

It was during a lull that Luis said behind him, 'You have seen Miss Grey, Rico?'

'No. Our little Linda said poof for your party—I will not

179

come.' Rico looked round. 'She meant it, Luis, but do not be angry with her.'

Luis looked at him as he might at a fly which had settled on his cuff. He called a servant. 'Tell Miss Grey we are waiting for her.'

Rico lifted his shoulders. 'She will not come down. I begged her, but she would promise only to toast us at ten o'clock, in privacy.'

Just perceptibly, Luis' jaw tightened. He bowed to a newly-arrived dowager and touched his lips to her wrist, made the customary gallant remark. The servant returned.

'Pardon, Senhor Marquez. There is only the maid on duty near the senhorito's bedroom. She says Miss Grey has gone out.'

Luis drew in his lip. To Rico, he said, 'Since you have made this appointment at ten o'clock, you perhaps have some notion of where she has gone.'

'For a walk outdoors, I should say.' Slightly puzzled and more than slightly anxious, Rico added, 'I think she was afraid you would insist that she come down early, so she has disappeared. I am quite sure she will return at ten. She always keeps a promise.'

'She is to come now,' said Luis, in controlled tones. 'She must be found.'

'But Luis, if she is not happy about this occasion.'

'Be silent!' was the brusque reply. 'Continue to welcome your guests.'

Luis moved away into the sala, came to a group which included Eve Bayes. He excused himself to the others, and addressed Eve.

'You have seen Miss Grey this evening, my dear Eve?'

'No,' rather quickly. 'No, I haven't. Is she missing?'

'She is possibly in the grounds.'

He bowed and went out to the terrace. The two servants were idle now, and he spoke to them. They had not seen Miss Grey, and thought it possible she had gone out the back way; she would not walk here among so many cars.

Luis strode along the terrace, paused at one of the open doors of the dining-room. In there, the two endlessly long tables glittered with gold and glass, with silver-gilt and white napery. The series of flower arrangements were a delight, even at a distance, but Luis didn't see them. He saw that only the servants were in there, waiting for nine o'clock. He was about to pass on when the chauffeur came up from the garden.

Luis turned. 'Pedro, you have seen Miss Grey?'

'No, Senhor Marquez. I have been rearranging the cars which have been parked so badly.'

'I wish her to be found. You will search the gardens on this side!'

'But, senhor, if I may mention it . . .'

'Yes?' said Luis sharply.

'Senhor Marquez, I think that perhaps Miss Grey has gone into the town. Yesterday I drove the senhorita to the market place and she came back in the car of Senhora Bayes. It was as they were parting . . .'

'Quick!'

'The chauffeur of Senhora Bayes does not understand English, but I heard the senhora say she would leave coffee and magazines for the senhorita tonight.'

'So!' It sounded like an imprecation, possibly upon Eve Bayes. 'Bring my car round quickly, Pedro. Leave it just beyond the cars—I will drive myself.'

He walked swiftly back into the sala, scarcely looked at Eve, but made his way towards the group who were entering from the hall. He drew Rico aside, said rapidly,

'I must go out for a short while. Do not forget in my absence that you are the host.'

'But Luis, it is twenty minutes to nine! Do we postpone the dinner?'

'For five minutes—no longer. If I am not back make my apologies and say that I have been called away but will not be long.'

'But where do you go?'

'Where else,' said Luis with suppressed violence, 'but to find Linda!'

Rico watched him go, looked down at his wide-eyed novia. 'He frightens me,' he said. 'I fly planes, Juanita, yet I am frightened by the look in the face of my own cousin! Would you say it is normal for a man to ignore a hundred guests while he searches for the nurse of his son?' She merely looked startled, and after a moment Rico patted her hand. 'I am thinking things, my little kitten—very wonderful things,' he said. 'I hope I am right!'

In the sitting-room of Mrs Bayes' villa Linda had made herself comfortable. She had tried to eat supper in the nursery with Jacinto, and failed. The excitement at the Palacio had run right through the place, and she had become keyed up by it herself, so that changing into the stiff white dress with the rosebud shoulder straps she had wondered whether it would not be better to brave the party for an hour rather than know the horrible ache of uncertainty all through the evening.

But somehow it had been easier to do as she had planned. At exactly eight-thirty she had gone out by the back staircase and slipped round the building to the drive. Within minutes, the Bayes had arrived, and the moment they had entered the reception hall she had got into their car. A quarter of an hour later she had closed herself in this room.

She poured coffee, but did not lift the napkin from the sandwiches. She lay back in a chaise-longue and looked at the carved wooden ceiling with its design of flowers at each corner. A weariness came into her limbs, a heaviness to her eyes. The coffee looked good, but tasted bitter on her tongue. Her arm was across the head of the long chair, and she turned her face on to it and wished her mind would cease its pulsing and become as tired as her body.

There were servants in the house, but she was terribly alone; she could not escape the coldness of her heart. Yet that was what she had to do. After all, only the expected was happening, and soon she would be away from it all. And she would never come back.

Her eyes pressed closer into her arm, the cornsilk hair fell forward in soft waves, and the whole of her body took the curve of the chaise-longue, so that she looked like a flower abandoned to sadness. And that was how Luis found her.

He had rung the bell through to the servants' quarters, had the door opened and an alarmed maid curtseying so low that she staggered as she rose. He gave the girl a perfunctory smile and said nothing, but walked straight into the sitting-room, where a single light illumined the slender white figure. He stood motionless for a second or two, came forward and sat down on the side of the long chair. He felt her become aware of him, saw her fingers shakily push at her hair while her back was still towards him.

He took her shoulders and turned her, looked at the large blue eyes fringed with wet lashes. He gave a small exclamation and slipped his arms around her.

'Tell me something very quickly. You weep for Cullum?'

'Of . . . course not.'

'And certainly not for Rico?'

'No. Oh, no.'

'Then you must come back with me at once. We cannot go into this now because I have left all the guests expecting a good dinner.' He stood up and drew her with him, took a folded handkerchief from his pocket. 'No sign of tears, please!' He paused as his glance lowered to her shoulders. 'You are dressed for the party. Why did you run away from it?'

Huskily she said, 'Rico insisted I should dress up to drink his health. Luis, I'd far rather stay here. You don't realise what . . .'

'I realise a great deal. Where there are English, things are apt to happen too fast, but we will deal with them. You have a wrap?'

'No, it's warmer tonight. Senhor . . .'

'A moment ago it was Luis. It is never again senhor. Now come quickly, or there will be two empty places at the table. No argument, I insist!'

She went with him, of course; there was no resisting that vital presence. He put her into the front seat of the car and turned so sharply in the road that she clung to the door-handle. They sped out of Merida at a pace that made conversation impossible. At the Palacio he ran the car on to a lawn, and came round to help her out. Automatically he drew her skirt clear and took her elbow.

From the courtyard it was possible to see that the sala had emptied, which meant that the guests had gone in to dinner. He led Linda through one of the glass doors into the sala, looked over her face in the brilliant light.

'Have no fear,' he said. 'You look very beautiful, very different.'

She swallowed. 'But I feel frightful. Please let me go now and come down after dinner. I promise . . .'

He seemed to withdraw slightly, and an odd tired look came into the dark eyes. 'This is important to me, very important. I am hoping it will also become important to you.' He offered his arm. 'Let us go in.'

Linda's knees shook as she entered the great dining-room with him. She saw the men rise, heard Luis' urbane, 'Please! I cannot apologise too humbly for this lateness. This child had lost herself and she had to be sought, but all is well now . . . we think.'

Linda found herself being seated to the left at the top of the table, next to Luis at the head. Dead opposite sat Nolette del Carros, wearing a charcoal gown of exquisite cut, a necklace of rubies, and a ruby-set comb in the immaculate black hair. The black eyes flashed across the table, the beautiful mouth smiled at Luis.

Linda couldn't help but refuse most of the dishes. She was swimming in some hazy emotion which seemed to have closed her throat right up. However, no one noticed but Luis, and he made no comment. He didn't even try very hard to include her in his conversation with Nolette and others.

It was just after she had declined one of the delicious fruit concoctions from a dumb-waiter that Nolette leaned forward and asked solicitously, and very clearly,

'You have had bad news, Miss Grey?'

'No,' said Linda.

She could feel that Nolette's question had created a slight tension in her immediate vicinity and that several people were looking at her. She put a hand towards her wine glass, hoping to look nonchalant, but her nerves were too tight to be trusted, and her fingers curled round into her palms.

Nolette followed up archly and loudly. 'You have even less colour than usual. Perhaps it is not the Englishman's departure but our warm climate which is to blame.'

Linda's hand on the table quivered, and the next second it was covered by Luis' in no mistakable fashion. It was strange how many people looked down the table and saw that strong, fleshless hand with the smaller, pale hand of the English girl almost obliterated inside it. Swift glances were exchanged, a dull red came up under the creamy skin of Nolette's neck and cheeks.

Very calmly, Luis said, 'Let us blame the lights for the pallor; they are not so kind to any of us as the candles to which we are accustomed at dinner. More wine, Nolette?'

The moment passed, and it was time for toasts. At last Doña Velira, at the other end of the table, rose to her feet. Everyone at both tables stood, and the women straggled after the majestic figure. But Luis caught Linda's arm as in a vice. With a courteous apology to his nearest male neighbour, he excused himself from the men's company, and led Linda down the room to one of the french doors. The dark glances followed them.

They were out in the terrace, walking round to the back of the Palacio, where guests would not venture, and taking the path which led down beside the lily-pool. And there he stopped and looked down at her, and perhaps fortunately for them both, she dropped her face forlornly into her hand; the small surrender robbed him of speech, so that he could only grip her and hold her closer and closer till she stopped trembling. Her head was still turned away from him, and his lips found her glistening shoulder, the curve of her neck.

'Please don't,' she choked. 'I'm grateful for what you've done . . . but don't!'

'I am not to hold you?' he said, his tones unfamiliarly thick. 'I have thought so often of how I would tell you I love you, but in those thoughts you have felt some love for me, too. I know you feel it, Linda. You must. Deus! This is insupportable. How does one convince an Englishwoman that there is no one else in the world, that there has never been another woman so loved and needed!'

While this penetrated, Linda was very still. Then, slowly, she lifted her head to look at him. She saw him in the darkness, the angular handsome face, his eyes with fire in them, his mouth just slightly parted as if . . . as if he were having almost as much difficulty in breathing as she was. Her defences were down, but she didn't know she was gazing at him with her heart in her eyes, an adoring, beseeching heart. She only knew that she had to reach up and hold on while her faint gasp died beneath his kisses. Those endless moments proved what she had felt she had always known; there could be no other lover anywhere such as Luis!

'Minha fé!' he exclaimed softly against her cheek. 'How I have longed for this. And how I have tried to keep it sufficiently at a distance until other things had been arranged! I love you so much, belíssima, but I have been so tied with this position we are in . . . and other things. You are very young, Lindasinha, and there is much about me you do not understand, much that I have to make you understand. Come to the other side of the pool and sit down!'

She moved lightly, like one in a dream, but as he lowered himself beside her she felt herself awakening, his vitality flowing into her. It was really true! This was Luis, who loved her. She felt him take her hand closely between both of his, his breath on her forehead as he talked, vibrantly.

'Because you are very English, this that I am going to say will amuse you. Tonight I held your hand on the dining table so that everyone could see; in the eyes of the people of Merida, who know me, that is a declaration. Funny, no?'

'Funny, yes,' she said. 'But . . . but it's beautiful. I didn't think you could possibly love me, Luis. I'm such an ordinary sort of . . .'

'If you are ordinary, my dearest heart, then these British are more amazing than I thought! I am sure that I loved you the first moment I saw you in my library, laughing with Rico; certainly I experienced in that moment the first of these unendurable pangs when you give attention to another man! But there has been so much with which to cope, as you say.' He gave a brief, despairing laugh. 'Here in Merida we go along year after year, knowing only the seasons and one another. In the Palacio there are only Doña Velira and myself, and our lives run smoothly between our duties and our friends. Then suddenly the whole atmosphere changes. One listens for a voice, finds disturbing the sight of a fair curly head and arranges to see it at lunch and at dinner! One even begins to look into a pair of blue eyes for something which is either not there or heavily veiled. Diabo! I have not known myself!'

Her voice shook as she said, 'I love you, Luis, but I . . . I'm not your kind. It always seemed . . .'

'Perhaps I know better than you think—the uncertainties and lack of understanding. But there was never a gulf between us; only a wall which was more of your making than mine. It was inevitable—just as it is inevitable that we break it down! That peace which existed at the Palacio before you came was a drugged kind of peace. I had never imagined that anyone like you could come into my life. But when you come, what happens?' He shrugged prodigiously. 'There is Rico, whom you encourage in his madness, Michael Cullum, whom I cannot possibly forbid you to see.'

'And my inconvenient plans for more freedom and fun for Jacinto!'

He was quiet for a minute, and his fingers tightened over her forearm. His face was in shadow now, and unreadable.

'Yes . . . Jacinto,' he said. 'It is not long since I realized that you have given him more love than I have ever done. I am afraid you must be told something of that marriage.'

'It isn't really necessary,' she said quickly.

'But it is—to me. It was one of those marriages you despise.

Amalia's parents and mine were the closest of friends and it had always been understood that we would marry. The engagement was announced while I was away at university, but it was several years later that we married.' He paused. 'There was no one else, you see, my dear one. Just Amalia, who was sweet and self-effacing, and who trusted me to take care of her and make her happy.'

Linda nodded wordlessly. She could see them; the gay, vital young Luis, and a dark girl who had probably loved him in her tranquil fashion but hadn't had nearly enough spirit and strength for such a union. It was strange, but she had always pitied Amalia, never been jealous of her.

He went on, 'Perhaps I never felt deeply for Jacinto because he reminded me of so much I had missed. And now it is through him that I have you here. I can never be grateful enough for that!'

'He admires you tremendously,' she said. 'We must both love him. Luis, are you going to send us to the sea?'

'The thought of it now makes me groan! The plan was for you and me, Linda. An excellent arrangement, if only you had collaborated. For everyone's sake, I cannot do quite as other men do. You feel I am too strict and conventional, but in such a society as ours it is unavoidable. I wanted you at the villa, where I could visit you often away from Merida. You could have engaged a new nurse—Portuguese or Spanish this time, as we already have enough of the British influence!—and we could have been alone a good deal. I am naturally anxious to meet your father, and I could imagine no more excellent idea than having him and your stepmother visit you at the coast for a period. That way, I, too, could have stayed at the villa, and the arrangements for marriage would have come swiftly and naturally. I still think it is the wise course, but I cannot bear to let you go.'

'But I will go,' she said at once. 'It'll make everything much easier for you.'

'No. Since we have now shown everyone that our marriage is inevitable, let it be soon. For me, it cannot be too soon! I will invite your parents here. We will be married and spend a month or two alone at the villa. You must agree, carissima!'

'Whatever you say, Luis,' she whispered. 'And ... and Nolette?'

He let out a sharp breath. 'She has gone too far, but I do not think she will trouble us after tonight. She is another who has helped in the building of the barrier between you and me.'

'Doña Velira thought you'd asked her to come home.'

'I did not, of course. The old Tia knew there was no one I cared for in Merida. Over the last two or three years she has been more and more troubled about me . . . you know how I mean. Where Nolette was concerned, Doña Velira merely hoped.'

'But Nolette did come here expecting you to marry her.'

'It may be true,' he said indifferently. 'Perhaps compared with some of the men she has met on her travels I am not such a bad bargain! She is obviously infatuated with the family jewels . . . those things which I brought here for you.'

'You did say you'd let her help to design the new settings!'

'I said it at a time, I believe, when I was in a condition to say anything that would pierce your tough little armour. It is possible that Nolette will now decide to carry out one of her ambitions. She has never yet studied and worked in London, but she has a new friend there now—Michael Cullum.' His tones altered, became low and impassioned. 'None of these people can touch us again. I knew that tonight something of this kind must happen; I have felt it all day. I adore you, my lovely Linda. I will always adore you!'

For a long while after that they were conscious only of each other, of lips and hands and heavily beating hearts.

But at last Linda said breathlessly, 'You'll have to go in, Luis. They'll wonder what on earth has happened to you!'

He laughed, the exultant laugh of a man who is masterfully and irrevocably in love. 'They will not wonder when they see us. It will take more than cosmetics to hide the evidence that you have been kissed. For me, I would not hide it for the world! But we will make no announcement until the guests are leaving. This is, after all, the evening of Juanita and Rico.'

But Linda knew that he felt as she did; that the night and the bright lights of the Palacio, the music, and that little boy sleeping peacefully away up there in the west wing, belonged exclusively to Luis and Linda.

Borne along at his side with her hand again in his, she thought of puppies and swings and see-saws, and Jacinto lording it over a couple of younger children. She quivered with tremulous laughter.

'A joke?' he asked gently.

'No, darling. Just heaven,' she told him.

A simple reply, but it compelled him to kiss her again, and to convince her anew that she had been created for the one purpose of bringing happiness to Luis Alvaro de Filano.

Doctor Nurse Romances

Don't miss
April's
other story of love and romance amid the pressure
and emotion of medical life.

MAJOR MIKE
by Hazel Fisher

When under Major Mike's command at the Territorial
Army camp, Nurse Lisa Hilton tries hard to ignore his
sarcastic comments, only to find she is haunted by the
Major's piercing dark eyes . . .

Order your copy today from your local paperback retailer.

Doctor Nurse Romances

Have you enjoyed these recent titles in our
Doctor Nurse series?

SISTER IN CHARGE
by Judith Worthy

When Nurse Dilys Davies decides to run the nursing
home left to her in her grandmother's will she does not
expect to find the raging village feud or the unpleasantness of the handsome local doctor . . .

MARRY ME, STRANGER
by Anne Vinton

Sister Laura Bradfield has a very hard time when she
agrees to work with the handsome but unpopular
Doctor Warwick. Things go from bad to worse, but not
before she discovers she is falling in love . . .

Order your copies today from your local paperback retailer.

Doctor Nurse Romances

and May's
stories of romantic relationships behind the scenes
of modern medical life are:

ACCIDENT WARD
by Clare Lavenham
When Nurse Joanne Marshall's boyfriend is admitted
to *her* ward, she is pleased to be able to nurse him
herself. But the handsome new registrar, Paul Vincent,
appears and her heart is torn in two . . .

HEAVEN IS GENTLE
by Betty Neels
Sister Eliza Proudfoot takes a job at Professor
Christian van Duyl's clinic and falls in love with him.
But then she finds he is already engaged to a placid
Dutch girl . . .

Order your copies today from your local paperback retailer.